ATOMIC AGE PHYSICS

FISSION OF URANIUM

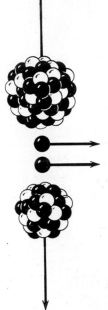

ATOMIC AGE
PHYSICS

HENRY SEMAT
Professor of Physics
The City College of New York

HARVEY E. WHITE
Professor of Physics
University of California

Rinehart & Company, Inc., New York

FOREWORD

Only in the recent past has man begun to probe the inner secrets of the atom. How atomic energy has affected military conduct is now common knowledge around the world. Less well known, however, is the potentiality of atomic resources for a richer and fuller life for all mankind. Although we read daily of new peaceful uses for atomic and nuclear energy, scientists themselves admit they are still on the threshold of significant discoveries. Before they can do more, they need to know more, and they need desperately an adequately trained body of additional scientists.

This need was underscored by the Russians' startling announcement that they had put a man-made earth satellite, Sputnik I, into orbit. In this country the response was instantaneous. The interest in science, which had grown tremendously in the previous dozen years, became even more intense. President Eisenhower urged greater emphasis on scientific training among the young. A distinguished scientist, Dr. James R. Killian, was recruited from Massachusetts Institute of Technology to head up a national science program. The demand for physicists, mathematicians, chemists, engineers, and other scientifically and technically trained personnel spread as never before through colleges, universities, research organizations, and even industry.

Not long after, during the summer of 1958, the National Broadcasting Company, in association with several foundations and public-spirited corporations, announced plans to help meet this need. To reach an audience of unprecedented size, it organized a nation-wide course in "atomic age physics." Hundreds of colleges across the country agreed to accept the NBC-TV course for credit, among them the nation's leading colleges for teacher training. It is out of this venture that the present volume grows.

This book closely follows the second half of the course,

though not designed to meet college-credit requirements. It contains, chapter by chapter, the lessons covered by the daily television lectures and demonstrations. It permits the non-credit observer to keep abreast of the course's progress even though an occasional program is missed. It is, moreover, an easy guide to the whole new science of atomics and nucleonics that should prove useful to any student, irrespective of his level of familiarity with the subject.

The book is divided roughly into two parts. The first ten chapters deal with the atom and atomic structure; the last seven dwell on the nucleus and nuclear structure. It begins with an examination of atomic particles and proceeds to explain their nature and behavior. Then it treats the nucleus in parallel manner. The final chapters of the book report the most recent nuclear achievements and point the way to future investigation.

Readers may use the book as they wish. For those with the basic mathematical background, the equations that have been included will illuminate the presentation of the theories. For those without the mathematics, the theories are clearly presented and may be pin-pointed even more sharply by reference to the many diagrams and illustrations prepared especially for this volume.

The authors believe this is the first thorough, easy-reading handbook for one of the most important and stimulating subjects of the day. Read alone, it will provide a solid course of instruction. In conjunction with the daily television sessions of *Continental Classroom*, it will prove an invaluable key to the scientific theories which will so strongly affect our future.

> *Henry Semat*
> *Harvey E. White*

New York City
January, 1959

CONTENTS

ATOMIC AGE PHYSICS

ATOMS
AND ELECTRONS

HISTORICAL BACKGROUND OF THE ATOMIC AGE

The first half of the twentieth century will go down undoubtedly as the Atomic Age both in science and in world affairs. Man's search for knowledge about the ultimate nature of matter goes back almost 2,500 years; it has been the work of scientists and philosophers during these twenty-five centuries that has brought that knowledge to its present state. The earliest awareness of a concept of atoms dates from Democritus (b. 460 B.C.) who imagined these particles to be indivisible and to be the constituents of all matter. The modern concept of an atom has rested on a sound scientific base since the early part of the nineteenth century.

In 1802, the English chemist John Dalton gave the modern notion of the atom its start by formulating the laws that govern the formation of *compounds* from a few simpler substances called *elements*. The ultimate particles of compounds were their *molecules*, while the ultimate particles of elements were *atoms*. Dalton in his experiments assumed that the atoms of any one element were identical in all respects. More recent investigations have shown that he was only partially right.

At the time of Dalton's work, only a comparatively small number of elements were known. As more elements were discovered, a distinct pattern—or grouping—of chemical properties among them became discerned. In 1869, Dmitri Mendeleev, a Russian chemist, made an important contribution to research by grouping the elements known at the time according to their properties. This arrangement is called the periodic table of the

The Chemical Elements

Element	Symbol	Element	Symbol
Actinium	Ac	Molybdenum	Mo
Aluminum	Al	Neodymium	Nd
Americium	Am	Neon	Ne
Antimony	Sb	Neptunium	Np
Argon	A	Nickel	Ni
Arsenic	As	Niobium (Columbium)	Nb
Astatine	At	Nitrogen	N
Barium	Ba	Osmium	Os
Berkelium	Bk	Oxygen	O
Beryllium	Be	Palladium	Pd
Bismuth	Bi	Phosphorus	P
Boron	B	Platinum	Pt
Bromine	Br	Plutonium	Pu
Cadmium	Cd	Polonium	Po
Calcium	Ca	Potassium	K
Californium	Cf	Praseodymium	Pr
Carbon	C	Promethium	Pm
Cerium	Ce	Protactinium	Pa
Cesium	Cs	Radium	Ra
Chlorine	Cl	Radon	Rn
Chromium	Cr	Rhenium	Re
Cobalt	Co	Rhodium	Rh
Copper	Cu	Rubidium	Rb
Curium	Cm	Ruthenium	Ru
Dysprosium	Dy	Samarium	Sm
Erbium	Er	Scandium	Sc
Europium	Eu	Selenium	Se
Fluorine	F	Silicon	Si
Francium	Fr	Silver	Ag
Gadolinium	Gd	Sodium	Na
Gallium	Ga	Strontium	**Sr**
Germanium	Ge	Sulfur	S
Gold	Au	Tantalum	Ta
Hafnium	Hf	Technetium	Tc
Helium	He	Tellurium	Te
Holmium	Ho	Terbium	Tb
Hydrogen	H	Thallium	Tl
Indium	In	Thorium	Th
Iodine	I	**Thulium**	Tm
Iridium	Ir	Tin	Sn
Iron	Fe	Titanium	Ti
Krypton	Kr	Tungsten	**W**
Lanthanum	**La**	Uranium	U
Lead	Pb	Vanadium	V
Lithium	Li	**Xenon**	Xe
Lutetium	Lu	Ytterbium	Yb
Magnesium	Mg	Yttrium	Y
Manganese	Mn	Zinc	Zn
Mendelevium	Mv	Zirconium	**Zr**
Mercury	Hg		

Periodic Table of the Elements

	I	II	III	IV	V	VI	VII	VIII		
1	1 H 1.0080							2 He 4.003		
2	3 Li 6.940	4 Be 9.013	5 B 10.82	6 C 12.011	7 N 14.008	8 O 16	9 F 19.00	10 Ne 20.183		
3	11 Na 22.991	12 Mg 24.32	13 Al 26.98	14 Si 28.09	15 P 30.975	16 S 32.066	17 Cl 35.457	18 A 39.944		
4	19 K 39.100	20 Ca 40.08	21 Sc 44.96	22 Ti 47.90	23 V 50.95	24 Cr 52.01	25 Mn 54.94	26 Fe 55.85	27 Co 58.94	28 Ni 58.71
4	29 Cu 63.54	30 Zn 65.38	31 Ga 69.72	32 Ge 72.60	33 As 74.91	34 Se 78.96	35 Br 79.916	36 Kr 83.80		
5	37 Rb 85.48	38 Sr 87.63	39 Y 88.92	40 Zr 91.22	41 Nb 92.91	42 Mo 95.95	43 Tc [99]	44 Ru 101.1	45 Rh 102.91	46 Pd 106.4
5	47 Ag 107.880	48 Cd 112.41	49 In 114.82	50 Sn 118.70	51 Sb 121.76	52 Te 127.61	53 I 126.91	54 Xe 131.30		
6	55 Cs 132.91	56 Ba 137.36	57–71 Rare Earths*	72 Hf 178.50	73 Ta 180.95	74 W 183.86	75 Re 186.22	76 Os 190.2	77 Ir 192.2	78 Pt 195.09
6	79 Au 197.0	80 Hg 200.61	81 Tl 204.39	82 Pb 207.21	83 Bi 209.00	84 Po 210	85 At [210]	86 Rn 222		
7	87 Fr [223]	88 Ra 226.05	89–101 Actinide† Series							

57 La 138.92	58 Ce 140.13	59 Pr 140.92	60 Nd 144.27	61 Pm [145]
62 Sm 150.35	63 Eu 152.0	64 Gd 157.26	65 Tb 158.93	66 Dy 162.51
67 Ho 164.94	68 Er 167.27	69 Tm 168.94	70 Yb 173.04	71 Lu 174.99

89 Ac 227	90 Th 232.05	91 Pa 231	92 U 238.07
93 Np [237]	94 Pu [242]	95 Am [243]	96 Cm [245]
97 Bk [249]	98 Cf [249]	99 E (Einsteinium)	100 Fm (Fermium)
101 Mv [256]			

* Rare Earth or Lanthanide Series.   † Actinide Series.

elements (see Table, page 3). Mendeleev placed elements with similar properties in the same vertical column. When he first constructed this table, Mendeleev left many spaces vacant and indicated that there were elements still to be discovered that would eventually fit into these places. The positions of the vacant spaces also suggested their probable chemical properties and thus aided in the search for the unknown elements.

The vacant spaces in the periodic table have now all been filled; moreover, elements beyond the heaviest then known have also been discovered. Some of them were found shortly after Mendeleev devised the periodic table; others were discovered only within the past two decades as a result of the advances made in the field of atomic and nuclear physics.

More than one hundred elements are known now. Some of these exist in large quantities and are quite common throughout the world. They include oxygen, hydrogen, silicon, nitrogen, and carbon. Others not quite so common exist only in isolated places; among these are gold, platinum, tin, uranium, and radium. A third category is not found in nature but is manufactured in atomic piles and in so called "atom-smashing" machines such as the cyclotron.

The concept of an atom as an indivisible particle began to give way in the latter half of the last century. At that time, the atom's essentially electrical character began to show itself. One way in which this became evident was through the chemical activity to be observed in reactions taking place in electrolytic cells—cells in which the atoms behaved as electrically charged particles, or *ions*. Another way was through the behavior of atoms in gases at low pressure when electric currents were passed through them. In these cases, small electrically charged particles—*electrons*—became detached from some atoms and added to others or were sent as free electrons through the electrical system. Reactions of this kind involved only comparatively small quantities of energy.

At the end of the nineteenth century, an entirely new type of phenomenon was discovered. Some atoms were found to disintegrate spontaneously through the emission of highly energetic, charged particles. This phenomenon known as *natural radioactivity*, discovered in 1896 by Henri Becquerel, Nobel prize-winning French physicist, revolutionized the whole concept of the atom. In the course of a few years it led to the development of the current view of the *nuclear structure of the atom.*

ATOMIC STRUCTURE

Beginning with the discoveries of x-rays in 1895 and radio-activity a year later, new phenomena and ideas emerged rapidly from many diverse sources of physics. Chronological development has little bearing on knowledge in this field. But for the growth of our knowledge of the structure of the atom let us note first the present view of the subject and second, by using a *flow sheet* (Figure 3), how and when new ideas and discoveries were brought to bear upon the concept of atomic structure.

The atom of any element consists of a complex pattern of electrons revolving about a massive, positively charged central core, called a *nucleus.* The nucleus is surrounded at comparatively great distances by a sufficient number of electrons to make the electrical charge of the complete atom zero, that is, the atom is electrically neutral. Under the action of the electrical forces between the nucleus of the atom and its electrons, the electrons move in almost circular orbits.

The nucleus itself consists of a certain number A of massive particles called *nucleons.* The symbol A also represents the *mass number of the atom.* There are two kinds of nucleons—*protons* and *neutrons.* Each of these has mass number 1. The neutron is electrically neutral, whereas the proton is positively charged. The charge of the proton, e, is equal and opposite to the charge of an electron, $-e$. But the mass of the proton is about 1,840 times the mass of an electron.

The number of protons in a nucleus is designated by the letter Z and is called the *atomic number of the atom.* The number of neutrons in the nucleus is called the *neutron number N.* Therefore, expressed as a mathematical formula:

$$A = Z + N.$$

Figure 1 gives some idea of the structure of a few atoms. A hydrogen atom of atomic number 1 and mass number 1—represented by the symbol $_1H^1$—consists of simply one proton in the nucleus and one electron moving in an orbit around the nucleus. A helium atom of $Z = 2$ and $A = 4$—represented by

$_2$He^4—is composed of two protons and two neutrons in the nucleus, and two electrons in an orbit or orbits circling the nucleus. A sodium atom—$_{11}$Na^{23}—of atomic number 11 and mass number 23 consists of a nucleus containing twenty-three nucleons, eleven of them protons and twelve neutrons, and eleven electrons in orbits surrounding the nucleus.

An element is composed of atoms all having the same atomic number, or the same number of protons in the nucleus. It may be designated in one of three ways—by a name, by a number, or by a letter symbol. Take sodium, for example: by name, it is sodium; by number, $Z = 11$; by letter symbol, Na (for its Latin name, *natrium*). The atoms of an element may actually differ from one another in the number of neutrons in the nucleus. Thus sodium might contain 10, 11, 12, or 13, etc. neutrons; correspondingly the mass numbers (A) would be 21, 22, 23, or 24, etc. ($Z + N$). A collection of atoms of any element all having the same mass number (A) is known as an istotope of the element. These isotopes differ from each other in their neutron numbers (N). Different isotopes of sodium, for instance, may be represented by $_{11}$Na^{21}, $_{11}$Na^{22}, and so forth.

An element found in nature may consist of one or more

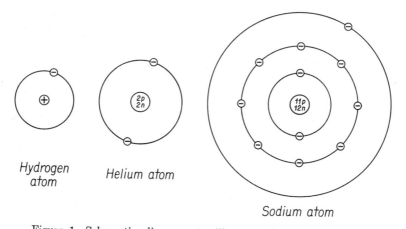

Hydrogen
atom   Helium atom

Sodium atom

Figure 1 Schematic diagrams to illustrate the structure of atoms. The innermost circle represents the nucleus; p is the symbol for a proton and n that for a neutron. An electron is represented by a small circle with a minus sign inside.

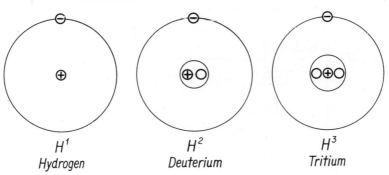

Figure 2   Three isotopes of hydrogen.

isotopes. Hydrogen, for example, has three isotopes of mass numbers 1, 2, and 3 (Figure 2). This element is so significant in both physics and chemistry that its three *isotopes* are sometimes called by distinct names. The isotope of mass number 1 is called *hydrogen*, that of $A = 2$ is *deuterium*, and the one of $A = 3$ is *tritium*. Even their nuclei have separate names and symbols. For hydrogen the nucleus is called *proton* (symbol p); for deuterium it is *deuteron* (symbol d), and for tritium it is *triton* (symbol t). In nuclear experiments these nuclei are used often as projectiles and fired at targets in the manner of bullets.

THE FLOW OF IDEAS

Discoveries and theories that have played prominent roles in the development of atomic and nuclear physics during the last sixty years may be studied in the flow sheet contained in Figure 3. The lefthand column lists those discoveries and ideas that have led to the comparatively complete knowledge we possess at present of the arrangement and distribution of electrons around the nuclei of atoms. In the column on the right are those pertaining directly to our less satisfactory knowledge of nuclear structure. The center column contains the new concepts in physics that differ radically from the more traditional ones which prevailed before 1900. These traditional concepts are sometimes called the concepts of classical physics. Most of the new concepts have contributed to our understanding of both electronic structure and nuclear structure. Many of these ideas have profoundly affected other fields of science such as solid state physics,

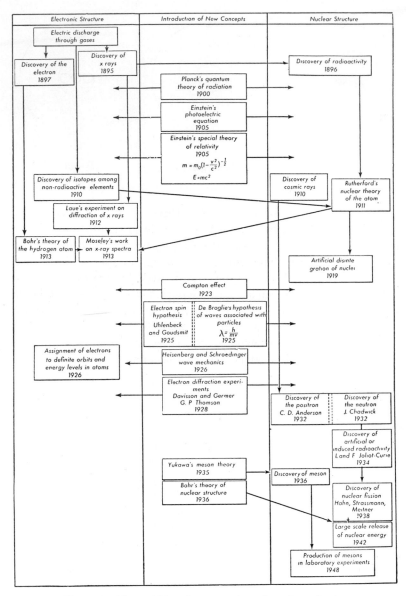

Figure 3 Flow of ideas into atomic and nuclear physics.

astrophysics, and chemistry. In addition, they have produced fundamental changes in our thinking about space, time, motion, and the nature of radiant energy.

The flow sheet is, in essence, a guide to the remainder of this book. If the reader wishes to know how a particular item under discussion fits into the general scheme of the book, he has only to refer to Figure 3.

ELECTRONS AND IONS

The study of electrical discharge through gases has been continuing since the days of Benjamin Franklin. Franklin was the first to show that lightning is a discharge of electricity through the air. With the development of vacuum pumps it became possible to observe the electrical discharge through gases at low pressures. Out of this study have come such outstanding events in the history of science as the discovery of the electron, the discovery of x-rays, the separation of isotopes of elements, sources of positive ions for high energy particle accelerators, and sources of light for various uses.

To study the passage of an electric current through a gas, let us put the gas into a long glass tube which has a circular electrode sealed into each end and which is provided with a small side tube that can be connected to a pumping system (Figure 4). This makes it possible to control the pressure of the gas in the tube.

Suppose that there is air in the tube and that the two electrodes A and C are connected, respectively, to the positive and negative terminals of a source capable of supplying 50,000 volts. When the pressure of the air inside the tube is reduced to a few millimeters of mercury, the passage of the electric current through the gas is accompanied by the emission of light from the gas. At this pressure the entire space between the electrodes is filled with a pink or reddish glow. The light you see is characteristic

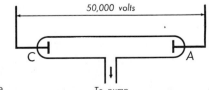

Figure 4   A gas-discharge tube.

of the gases in the tube. Such tubes are in commercial use as sources of light for various purposes. They are very valuable in the physics laboratory as a means of studying the spectra—that is, the composition of the light emitted by various elements and compounds.

When the pressure of the air in the tube is reduced to about 0.1 mm., the uniform glow between the electrodes disappears and a series of dark and light regions takes its place (Figure 5). A bluish velvety glow, known as the *cathode glow,* covers the entire negative electrode, or cathode *C*. This is followed by a dark space called the *Crookes dark space* which ends at the *negative glow.* The negative glow is separated by the *Faraday dark space* from the luminous column, known as the *positive column.* The positive column extends to the positive electrode, or anode *A*. The positive column usually appears to be striated; that is, it consists of a series of bright and dark zones. Covering the entire anode, or positive terminal, is the *anode glow.*

Experiments show that there are always some ions present in the air. These ions may have been produced by the action of light. They may result from collisions between molecules, or from ionizing agents which are ever present at the earth's surface and are known as *cosmic rays.* Irrespective of the original source of these ions, they are set in motion when several thousand volts are put across the electrodes *A* and *C*; the positive ions move toward *C*, the negative ions toward *A*. If the pressure of the gas is approximately 1 atm (1 atm = 760 mm. of mercury) these ions, on the average, move through very short distances before colliding with neutral atoms or molecules. Under these circum-

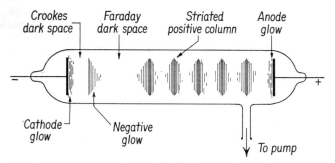

Figure 5   Appearance of electrical discharge when the pressure of the air in the tube is about 0.1 mm of mercury.

stances, they will have acquired little energy between collisions. But when the pressure is reduced to 1 mm. of mercury, these ions travel comparatively longer distances between collisions and, under the action of the electric field, they acquire more energy during their motion.

When an ion with sufficient energy collides with a neutral atom or molecule, it may succeed in knocking out an electron from the neutral atom or molecule and still retain enough kinetic energy to move away. In so doing, it leaves two additional charges in the gas: the electron, and the ionized atom or molecule. This process is called *ionization by collision*. As the pressure is lowered, a greater number of collisions result in the production of ions and electrons. At the same time, of course, some of the positive and negative charges recombine to form neutral atoms or molecules.

When the pressure of the gas in the tube gets very low, the average distance that an ion or electron travels between collisions becomes relatively large and the number of collisions it can make becomes small. Some of the charges may even travel the entire length of the tube without making any collisions with the molecules of the gas. At such low pressures of about 0.001 mm. of mercury, the positive ions which reach the cathode have a great amount of energy. One result is that the cathode, under bombardment of the positive ions, gives off electrons. These are sometimes called *cathode rays* because of their origins. They leave the cathode in a direction perpendicular to its surface.

DISCOVERY OF THE ELECTRON

A Nobel prize-winning English physicist, J. J. Thomson, was the first to determine the nature of the cathode rays. Thomson, in 1897, measured the ratio of a cathode ray's charge e to its mass m. He did so by sending cathode rays through electric and magnetic fields. Subsequently, many other scientists performed similar experiments on both cathode rays and electrons from other sources. Every study showed that cathode rays and electrons were the same thing.

In Thomson's experiment (Figure 6), the cathode rays travel from the cathode C to the anode A because of the action of the electric field that exists in the space between them. The electric

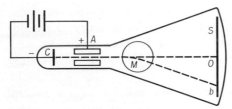

Figure 6 Tube for meas-
uring the ratio of *e/m* of
cathode rays.

field is produced by connecting C and A to the terminals of a battery or other source of electrical energy. The *strength of this electric field* is expressed by the ratio V/d, in which V is the *difference of potential* of the source, commonly called the voltage, and d is the distance from C to A. (Difference of potential is the work done per unit charge in transferring a charge of electricity from one point to the other.) In this case the work done is Ve, in which e is the charge of the electron.

The negative charge e forced to move from the cathode to the anode acquires additional kinetic energy thereby. This energy equals $\frac{1}{2}mv^2$— m is the mass of the particle and v its speed.

The electron, having gained this energy, then passes through a hole in the anode into a region containing a magnetic field. This field is maintained at the proper strength by an electromagnet M whose poles are on opposite sides of the tube used in the experiment. When a charged particle enters this magnetic field with its velocity at right angles to the direction of the field, the particle is forced to move in a circular path. The radius of the path is in direct proportion to the mass of the particle m and its velocity v, but in inverse proportion to the strength of the magnetic field, represented by the symbol B.

When the magnetic field is comparatively weak, the radius of the circular path is large; the electrons are then deflected through a small angle and they strike the fluorescent screen of the cathode ray tube at some point b below O. The radius of the path of the electron can be calculated from the amount of deflection. The strength of the magnetic field can be measured by any standard method, while the difference in potential from C to A is measurable with a voltmeter. All these quantities can thus be determined and used to find the ratio of the charge of a cathode ray to its mass—e/m.

Measurements of e/m, the ratio of the charge to mass, of electrons from all types of sources yield practically the same

Figure 7 J. J. Thomson (1856-1940). Discovered the electron. He was the first to separate the isotopes of non-radioactive elements. (*Courtesy of Culver Service.*)

value, if their velocity is small in comparison with the speed of light. The present accepted value is

$$e/m = 1.759 \times 10^8 \text{ coulombs/gram.}$$

(A coulomb is the practical unit of electric charge. If one coulomb of charge passes a given region per second, the current through this region is called one ampere.)

Thomson's method has been applied in a variety of ways and in modified forms to many scientific and practical devices. Its adaptation has brought about the development of all kinds of objects from the television tube in your home to the largest atom-smashers. The value of Thomson's contribution to modern physics can hardly be overestimated.

CHARGE OF THE ELECTRON

The Thomson experiment gives us only the ratio of the charge to the mass of the electron. It does not provide the values of the charge or the mass. To find e and m separately, we must conduct another experiment.

Robert A. Millikan, an American physicist, supplied that experiment. He was the first to make precise determinations of the electronic charge e. Millikan's apparatus consisted of two brass plates approximately 22 cm. in diameter set 1.5 cm. apart, with air all around them. He enclosed the plates in a box to shield them from air currents and to keep the pressure and temperature in this space constant (Figure 8). Then he sprayed small drops of oil from an atomizer into the box and eventually one small drop drifted through the opening C in the upper plate A. Since air resists any motion through it, the drop of oil moved downward with a speed that quickly reached a uniform value v which was governed by its weight mg and the properties of the air, such as its temperature and pressure.

In this experiment, the motion of the oil drop is observed through a telescope. The velocity can be determined by timing the drop's passage through a fixed distance set by the positions of two cross hairs in the telescope. The oil drop is charged with charge q when it leaves the atomizer. If the terminals of a battery are now connected to plates A and B, the drop of oil experiences an additional force

$$F = \frac{V}{d}q.$$

By adjusting the difference of potential of the plates this force can be made equal and opposite to the weight of the oil drop. However, Millikan's experiment does not rely on this procedure for determining the electronic charge.

During his investigations, Millikan observed that on occasion the oil drop would suddenly change its velocity. Sometimes there was a gain and sometimes a loss of speed. Millikan reasoned that these changes resulted from the oil drop acquiring either positive or negative ions from the neighboring air. By measuring the change in velocity he was able to compute the amount of electric charge added or lost by the drop. In addition, he ionized the air by means of x-rays and by radiations from radioactive materials, and then measured the gain or loss of charge from the change in velocity of the oil drop.

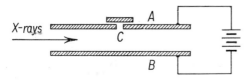

Figure 8 Schematic diagram of Millikan's apparatus for determining the charge of an electron.

Figure 9 Robert A. Millikan (1868-1953). Made accurate determinations of the charge of the electron and the value of the Planck constant h. (*Courtesy of* The American Journal of Physics. *Copyright Harris & Ewing.*)

From many measurements of this kind using oil drops of different weights and under a variety of conditions, Millikan concluded that in each case the gain or loss of charge by the drop of oil was always a whole multiple of a fundamental charge— the charge e equivalent to that of an electron. The charge had the same value whether it was positive or negative, since a loss of a positive charge produced the same effect as the gain of a negative charge by the oil drop. The present accepted value of the electronic charge e, is

$$e = 1.602 \times 10^{-19} \text{ coulomb.}$$

MASS OF THE ELECTRON

Since we know the charge of the electron—$e = 1.602 \times 10^{-19}$ coulomb—and we also know the ratio of the charge e to its mass m from independent experiments

$$\frac{e}{m} = 1.759 \times 10^8 \text{ coul/gm}$$

we can easily find the mass of the electron, which is

$$m = 9.106 \times 10^{-28} \text{ gm.}$$

The mass of the electron is very small. It is only 1/1840 of the mass of the lightest atom known—hydrogen. Thus the electrons of an atom contribute a negligible amount to its mass. The mass of an atom is concentrated almost entirely in its nucleus.

NOTATION IN POWERS OF TEN

The significance of very large numbers, and also that of very small numbers, may become obscured because of the large number of figures or of zeros that are needed to express them in the ordinary notation. A more convenient method of notation for both large and small numbers is the use of powers of 10 to indicate the position of the decimal point. The notation will become evident by an inspection of the following tables.

For large numbers, we can write

$$
\begin{aligned}
1 &= 10^0 \\
10 &= 10^1 \\
100 &= 10^2 \\
1,000 &= 10^3 \\
10,000 &= 10^4 \\
100,000 &= 10^5 \\
1,000,000 &= 10^6 \\
10,000,000 &= 10^7 \quad \text{and so forth.}
\end{aligned}
$$

For small numbers, we can write

$$
\begin{aligned}
0.1 &= 10^{-1} \\
0.01 &= 10^{-2} \\
0.001 &= 10^{-3} \\
0.0001 &= 10^{-4} \\
0.00001 &= 10^{-5} \\
0.000001 &= 10^{-6} \\
0.0000001 &= 10^{-7} \quad \text{and so forth.}
\end{aligned}
$$

For example, the speed of light is

$$c = 29{,}979{,}000{,}000 \text{ cm/sec} = 2.9979 \times 10^{10} \text{ cm/sec.}$$

As another example

$$1 \text{ Mev} = 0.0000016 \text{ erg} = 1.6 \times 10^{-6} \text{ erg.}$$

2 THERMIONIC AND PHOTOELECTRIC EFFECTS

Many fundamental experiments leading to new ideas and discoveries in atomic and nuclear physics require a large supply of electrons that can be controlled easily with respect to number and energy. One source meeting this specification has already been described, the electric discharge through gases. An even more important source is the emission of electrons by hot bodies. It is called *thermionic emission*.

Thermionic emission of electrons was discovered in 1883 by Thomas A. Edison while he was trying to improve the efficiency of the incandescent lamp he had invented a few years before. In the course of experimenting with the lamp, Edison inserted a metal plate in the globe enclosing the filament and then pumped out the glass enclosure to create a vacuum. He observed that when the filament of the lamp was heated and the plate was connected outside the globe to the positive side of the filament, electric charges flowed from the filament to the part of the plate inside. But when the plate was connected to the negative side of the filament, no flow of charge occurred.

The concept of electrons had not yet been formulated at the time of Edison's observation. Only twenty years later did A. J. Fleming patent the first practical thermionic tube as a rectifier and detector of radio waves. This type of tube has remained in use to the present, a two-element tube known as a *diode*. A few years later, Lee DeForest added a third electrode—a *grid*—to the tube, making possible its use as an amplifier and as a generator of high frequency alternating currents required for radio, radar, and television.

Figure 1 illustrates the kind of electric circuit used in the study of thermionic emission. The diode which is shown diagrammatically consists of a filament F and a metallic plate P, both sealed in a vacuum tube. The filament is heated by electric current from a battery A. Another battery B and a galvanometer G are connected in series between the plate and one side of the filament. When the positive terminal of B is connected to the plate, a current flows through the circuit, but when the negative terminal of B is connected, no current flows through the circuit; the galvanometer which registers the current reads zero.

The explanation of this behavior is that the filament when heated gives off negative electrons; hence, each time the plate is positive in relation to the filament, the electrons become attracted to the plate and flow through the circuit to the filament. When, however, the plate is negative in relation to the filament, the plate repels the electrons with the result that no current flows in the circuit.

If the filament is heated to a given temperature T, some of the free electrons of the metal evaporate from the filament into the space surrounding it. These form an *electron gas* around the filament. A state of equilibrium results when as many electrons leave the filament as re-enter it from the electron gas around it. When a difference of potential exists between the filament and the plate, electrons are attracted to the plate and other electrons evaporate from the filament to replace them. If the voltage becomes large enough, the electrons move to the plate as fast as the filament gives them off. A further increase in plate voltage does not increase the current through the tube.

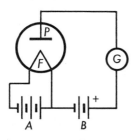

Figure 1 Circuit for showing thermionic emission.

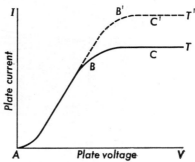

Figure 2   Curves showing the thermionic current as a function of the voltage at different filament temperatures.

Figure 2 shows the plate current I as a function of the difference of potential between the plate and filament. At first I increases as V does. But starting at point b, any additional increase of V does not produce a corresponding change in current. This level of current reached at b is the *saturation current*; in any single filament, the saturation current depends on temperature. If the temperature of a filament is raised from T to T', the saturation level of the current also rises.

THE PHOTOELECTRIC EFFECT

From time to time an experiment conducted to test or verify one idea leads unexpectedly to some entirely new concept or idea, or even to a new branch of physics. This is precisely what happened in 1887 when a German physicist named Heinrich Hertz tried to demonstrate the accuracy of the idea that light was propagated as an electromagnetic wave.

The idea was first proposed in 1864 by James C. Maxwell, a Scotsman. Twenty-three years later, Hertz succeeded in producing electromagnetic waves by using a high frequency alternating current fed into a circuit in which an electric spark moved through the air from one spherical electrode to another. In seeking to enlarge the size of the spark, he permitted ultraviolet light to fall on the spark gap and noted that the gap thus became a better conductor.

In the year following Hertz's experiment, Hallwachs pushed the investigation further by allowing ultraviolet light to fall on a zinc plate connected to an electroscope (Figure 3), an instru-

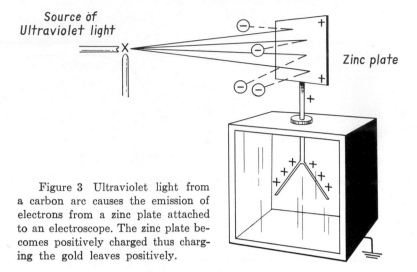

Figure 3   Ultraviolet light from
a carbon arc causes the emission of
electrons from a zinc plate attached
to an electroscope. The zinc plate becomes positively charged thus charg-
ing the gold leaves positively.

ment that measures minute charges of electricity. When the zinc
plate was charged negatively, the ultraviolet light striking its
surface caused the zinc plate to lose its charge. But when the
plate was positively charged, no loss of charge resulted from the
action of the light.

From this experiment it became evident that only negative
charges were emitted by or ejected from the surface of the zinc
plate because of the action of ultraviolet light.

This phenomenon is known as the *photoelectric effect*. The
negative charges emitted in the photoelectric effect are known
now to be electrons; they are sometimes called *photoelectrons*.

ENERGY OF THE PHOTOELECTRONS

The photoelectric effect has been subjected to intensive study
because of its significance in the development of new ideas and
concepts in atomic and nuclear physics, and also because of its
many practical applications. Figure 4 illustrates a typical photoelectric tube. In it, P is the photoelectric surface and A indicates
a wire used as an anode to collect the photoelectrons emitted by
P when light falls on it. The photoelectric current—the number
of electrons per second that move from P to A—is measured by

a galvanometer G which is connected in series with P, A, and a battery B. The tube that contains both P and A has as good a vacuum as possible.

The photoelectric current is shown by experiment to be directly proportionate to the intensity of the light, that is, to the amount of radiation falling on a unit area of P in a given unit of time. This means that the number of electrons emitted per second is in proportion to the intensity of the light.

Measurement of the kinetic energy of the photoelectrons shows that this energy depends on the nature of the light, not on its intensity. That is, it depends on the wavelength—or frequency —of the light.

In a series of very careful experiments in 1916, Millikan used sodium and potassium as the photoelectric surfaces. These were illuminated by light of different wavelengths. Millikan found the maximum kinetic energy of the photoelectrons, $\frac{1}{2}mv^2_{max}$, for each wavelength by measuring the negative voltage V_0 on the anode A necessary to reduce the photoelectric current to zero.

The results of Millikan's experiment are best represented by a graph (Figure 5). In the graph, the maximum kinetic energy of the emitted photoelectrons is plotted along the vertical axis and the frequency ν of the falling light is plotted along the horizontal

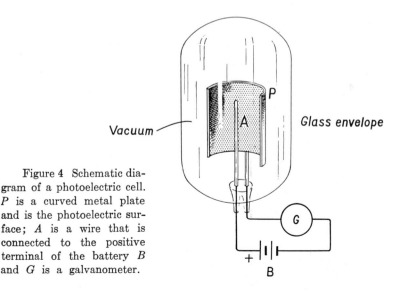

Figure 4 Schematic diagram of a photoelectric cell. P is a curved metal plate and is the photoelectric surface; A is a wire that is connected to the positive terminal of the battery B and G is a galvanometer.

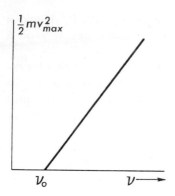

Figure 5 Graph showing the dependence of the maximum kinetic energy of the photoelectrons on the frequency of the incident light.

axis. For any particular metallic surface, the graph is a straight line. It may be written as the following equation:

$$\tfrac{1}{2}mv^2{}_{max} = h\nu - h\nu_0.$$

In the equation, h represents the slope of the line and ν_0 is the smallest frequency of light that can cause the emission of an electron from the particular surface under study. The limiting frequency ν_0 is called the *threshold frequency* of the substance in question.

The slope of the line h is a constant. It is wholly independent of the nature of the surface. The constant h, known as the *Planck constant*, plays a highly important role in atomic phenomena. Its accepted value at the present time is

$$h = 6.625 \times 10^{-27} \text{ erg sec.}$$

EINSTEIN'S PHOTOELECTRIC EQUATION

The dependence of a photoelectron's energy on the frequency of the incident radiation—the striking light rays—is not explicable on the basis of the electromagnetic wave theory of light. The wave theory requires a relationship between the intensity of the incident light and the energy of the photoelectron; this counters the observations of the photoelectric effect. The first explanation of the photoelectric effect dates back to 1905 when Albert Einstein made use of the concept of a *quantum of energy*—a concept introduced five years earlier by Max Planck to explain the distribution of energy among the many wavelengths in the radiation from a "black body"—that is, a body that absorbs all the radiation falling on it—at a high temperature.

According to Planck's theory, the energy $\mathscr{E}$ of a quantum, or elemental unit, of radiant energy is in direct proportion to the frequency of the radiation. Thus

$$\mathscr{E} = h\nu$$

in which h is the constant of the direct proportion, the Planck constant. The quantum of radiant energy $h\nu$ is also called a *photon*. In Einstein's explanation of the photoelectric effect, a single electron is cast off from the metal by the action of a single photon (Figure 6); the photon loses all of its own energy in the process. Some of this energy p is used to separate the electron from the metal.

By applying the principle of conservation of energy to the process, the electron comes out of the metal surface with a kinetic energy expressed by the equation

$$\tfrac{1}{2}mv^2 = h\nu - p.$$

This equation is known as *Einstein's photoelectric equation*. In it m represents the mass of the electron and v its speed. For electrons ejected from the metal with maximum kinetic energy, the value of p is a minimum and is expressed as $p = h\nu_0$.

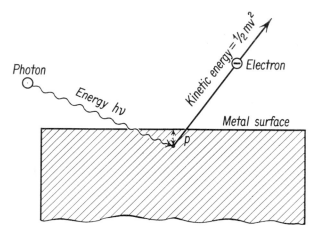

Figure 6 A photon ejects an electron from the surface of a metal.

The Einstein photoelectric equation thus becomes identical with the equation for the straight-line graph in Figure 5.

The photoelectric effect is not limted to the action of light on metallic surfaces. It can occur also in gases, liquids, and solids. The radiation that is capable of producing the photoelectric effect embraces the whole range of electromagnetic waves from the very short gamma rays and x-rays to the very long infra-red rays. Study of the kinetic energies of the photoelectrons involved in the photoelectric effect enables us to find the values of p and in consequence opens the door to significant information about the origins of the photoelectrons.

SECONDARY EMISSIONS OF ELECTRONS

The atoms of a solid are so close together that some of the outer electrons are shared by neighboring atoms or, in the case of metals, they may even travel freely from one atom to another. This is so because of the electric forces that exist between the electrons and nuclei of neighboring atoms. The *free electrons* or, better, *conduction electrons* average about one or two to the atom. They can be removed by applying enough energy to them. We have examined two methods for accomplishing this: by heating the metal as in the thermionic effect, or by the action of radiant energy as in the photoelectric effect.

Another method, which has important practical applica-

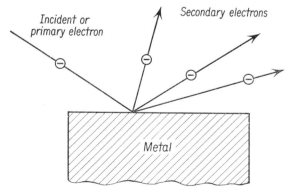

Figure 7   A primary electron may eject one or more secondary electrons from a metal.

tions, is to provide the energy by bombarding the metal with electrons from some other source (Figure 7). The incident electrons, also called *primary electrons*, bombard the solid under this method causing the ejections of *secondary electrons*. Unlike the photoelectric effect in which a single photon causes the emission of only one electron, a primary electron may impel the emission of several secondary electrons from the solid. The ratio of the number of secondary electrons to the number of primary electrons varies from one to five; this depends on the nature of the solid and the energy of the primary electrons. The minimum energy required of a primary electron to produce a secondary electron is approximately 10 electron volts.

Secondary electrons vary widely with respect to energy. Their range of energy depends on the energy of the primary electron and on the energies of the electrons in the solid. The emission of secondary electrons has many applications in the design of thermionic tubes used in radio and television and in the development of the *photomultiplier tube* used extensively in nuclear physics.

THE PHOTOMULTIPLIER TUBE

A photomultiplier tube is an extremely sensitive photoelectric tube containing a high gain amplifier. To operate it requires secondary electron emission from additional electrodes built into the tube. Figure 8 is a schematic diagram of the design of a photomultiplier tube. In this design, P represents the photosensitive cathode. Light striking P forces the ejection of photoelectrons from it. A difference of potential of about 100 volts exists between P and the first electrode, usually called a *dynode*. As the photoelectron strikes the dynode, it induces the emission of several secondary electrons. In the figure the ratio of secondary to primary electrons is four to one. Moreover, there are five dynodes, each maintained at a potential of 100 volts more than the preceding one, with secondary emission taking place at each of these.

Suppose that a photoelectron strikes dynode 1, producing R electrons, R representing the ratio of secondary to primary electrons. If this same ratio is maintained at each successive dynode,

dynode 2 will emit R^2 electrons, dynode 3 will emit R^3 electrons, and the last or nth dynode will emit R^n. Modern photomultiplier tubes contain ten to sixteen dynodes. The electrons from the nth dynode go to the anode A, whence they pass to a detecting circuit.

Some idea of the magnification produced by a photomultiplier tube may be observed by giving R a value of 4 and n a value of 10. This assignment of values results in a gain of 1,000,000 for the tube (4^{10} = approximately 1,000,000). Thus, if a single photon produces one electron at the photosensitive cathode P, 1,000,000 electrons will reach the anode. This is a fully measurable charge. Some high-gain photomultiplier tubes have been built with multiplication factors of one billion.

Photomultiplier tubes used in connection with any of several fluorescent materials known as *phosphors* are now used extensively for detection and counting of photons and high energy particles such as electrons, protons, alpha particles, and other nuclear and subnuclear entities. Together with appropriate counting and analyzing circuits, these devices are called *scintillation counters*.

Figure 9 depicts a phosphor mounted on a photomultiplier tube in use as a scintillation counter. If some radiation penetrates the aluminum foil to produce a scintillation at some point S, the light from it will strike the photocathode either directly or after

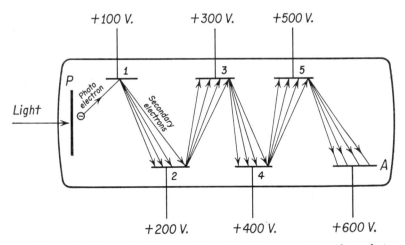

Figure 8 Schematic diagram illustrating the operation of a photomultiplier tube with five dynodes. Four secondary electrons are assumed to be emitted for each electron striking a dynode.

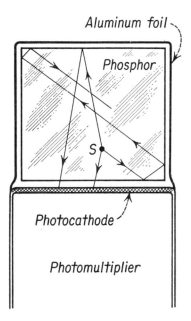

Figure 9 Light coming from a scintillation S may be reflected many times to reach the photocathode of the photomultiplier tube.

reflection from the aluminum. The value of a phosphor as a scintillation counter is contingent on the shortness of the duration of the light pulse emitted at S. The duration of the light pulse is about 10^{-8} second (one one hundred-millionth of a second) in phosphors suitable as scintillation counters.

3 MASS AND ENERGY

ENLARGING THE CONCEPT OF ENERGY

The existence of virtually limitless amounts of hitherto unknown sources of energy first became apparent as a consequence of the Einstein theory of relativity. One outgrowth of this famous theory has been the development of an entirely new idea about the relationship between mass and energy. This idea which has been verified again and again since its inception is that *mass is a form of energy* and that all known forms of energy have mass.

In physics, the various branches of the science form a unified body of knowledge through a set of general laws known as *conservation laws*. The better known of these include the law of conservation of energy, the law of conservation of momentum, and the law of conservation of electric charge. Whenever a new idea or concept is introduced, or a new phenomenon is discovered, it is desirable to incorporate it into the existing laws. But, as scientists, we must be prepared and willing at any time to change these laws, if necessary, or to replace them by new ones. Einstein's special or restricted theory of relativity has forced such a choice on physics, and physicists have enlarged the law of conservation to include mass as a form of energy.

Einstein's theory has played so fundamental a part in the development of atomic and nuclear physics that it seems advisable to digress a little to examine its historical basis and some of its results.

SPECIAL THEORY OF RELATIVITY

The Einstein theory of special or restricted relativity is one of the most important developments in twentieth-century physics. It emerged from the failure of all attempts to show that the motion of a source of light in relation to an observer had any effect on the speed of light. One of the best of these was an experiment by Michelson and Morley in 1887 that used an instrument known as an interferometer (Figure 1).

In the Michelson-Morley experiment, light from a source S strikes a half-silvered mirror A at an angle of 45°. Part of the light is transmitted to mirror B and reflected to A. The remainder is reflected to mirror C and then back to A. The two beams meet at A where they produce a set of interference fringes viewable through a telescope. The entire apparatus is mounted on a rigid platform that can be rotated about an axis perpendicular to the plane of the instrument.

Suppose that the interferometer is set in a position that makes the arm AB parallel to the velocity v of the earth through space at any time. Suppose further that c is the speed of light in space or in some hypothetical *aether* assumed to fill all space. On the Newtonian or classical theory, the velocity of light relative to the instrument along AB is $c - v$ forward and $c + v$

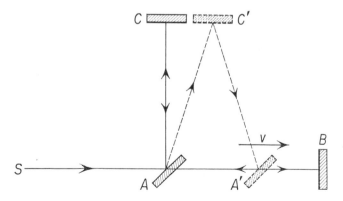

Figure 1 Schematic diagram of the Michelson-Morley experiment. The velocity of the earth through the aether is represented by v. The path of the ray of light ACA is actually that shown by the dotted lines $AC'A'$.

when reflected. The velocity of light along AC is $\sqrt{c^2 - v^2}$. If the lengths of AB and AC are equal, the time lapse in the movement of the beam of light from A to B and back will differ from the time it takes to travel from A to C and back.

In the experiment, the positions of the interference fringes were noted in the telescope when the interferometer was so placed that AB paralleled the earth's velocity. Then the instrument was rotated 90° to make AC parallel to the earth's velocity and AB perpendicular to it. Since the times of travel of the two light-beams differed, a shift in the positions of the fringes should have occurred. Yet no shift was observed within the limits of accuracy of the experiment.

On the basis of classical mechanics and electromagnetism, the results, or lack of results, of the experiment are impossible to account for. But according to Einstein, these results can be explained by assuming that *the speed of light is a constant and is independent of the motion of the source and of the observer.* This statement forms the *first postulate* of the theory of special or restricted relativity. The *second postulate* of the theory is that *all systems which are in uniform motion relative to one another are equally valid frames of reference, and that the fundamental physical laws must have the same mathematical forms in each of these reference frames.*

Einstein examined the basic concepts and ideas of physics in the light of the postulates of his theory. At the time the results were startling, but since then, 1905, they have become fully accepted and incorporated into the science of physics.

Suppose that the length of a rigid bar AB is measured by an observer who is at rest with respect to it and that the length is found to be L_0. Then suppose that the length of the same bar is measured by a second observer who is moving parallel to the length of the bar with a velocity v. This observer calls the length L. Comparing results, the two observers find that L is less than L_0. The relationship between the two lengths measured by the two observers, according to the Einstein theory, is expressed by the following equation:

$$L = L_0 \, (1 - v^2/c^2)^{\frac{1}{2}}.$$

In this equation c signifies the speed of light.

A phenomenon of this kind was anticipated by G. F. Fitzgerald and H. A. Lorentz, and was used by them to explain the results of the Michelson-Morley experiment. They suggested that the dimensions of the system in motion contracted along the direction of that motion enough to compensate for the change in speed of light along the path.

The concept of time also undergoes a significant change. If two clocks are identical, one at rest with respect to an observer and the other moving with uniform velocity with respect to him, the moving clock will run slower.

RELATIVE VELOCITIES IN THE SPECIAL THEORY OF RELATIVITY

In view of the change in the fundamental concepts of length and time, it is to be expected that the concept of relative velocity should also change. Under the older principles of Newtonian mechanics, if a particle P is moving with a constant velocity w in relation to a frame of reference that is itself moving with another velocity u relative to some observer, P's velocity v relative to the observer is expresed in the equation

$$v = u + w.$$

On the basis of the Einstein theory of relativity this equation becomes modified to

$$v = \frac{u + w}{1 + uw/c^2}$$

The relativistic value is smaller than the Newtonian value (Figure 2).

When u and w are small in comparison with the velocity of light c, the second of these two equations reduces to the first. As an interesting application of the equation of relative velocities, consider the case of a source of light such as an atom or a star moving with a velocity u relative to an observer on the earth (Figure 3). The speed of the light relative to the source is $w = c$. To measure the velocity of this light relative to the observer on earth, let us substitute c for w in the previous equation, since $w = c$. The result is

$$v = \frac{u + c}{1 + uc/c^2}$$

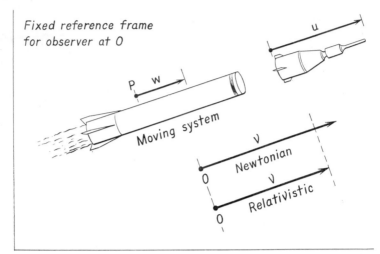

Figure 2   The velocity v relative to an observer O of the head of a rocket which is moving with a velocity u relative to the body of the rocket when the latter is moving with velocity w relative to the observer.

which becomes

$$v = \frac{u - c}{1 - u/c}$$

from which $v = c$.

This result is to be expected. That is because the equation for relative velocities is derived on the basis of the postulates of the special theory of relativity, specifically the one that stipulates the velocity of light c is independent of the motion of the source or the observer. An important conclusion, therefore, to be drawn from the special theory of relativity is that no material particle can have a speed in excess of the speed of light, and no signal or energy can be transmitted at a speed greater than the speed of light.

VARIATION OF MASS WITH VELOCITY

Before Einstein published his theory of relativity, the concepts of mass and energy were independent of each other. It was assumed that the mass of a body was a property of that body,

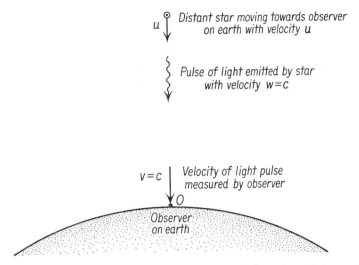

u Distant star moving towards observer
on earth with velocity u

Pulse of light emitted by star
with velocity $w = c$

$v = c$ Velocity of light pulse
measured by observer

O

Observer
on earth

Figure 3 The velocity of light is a constant c independent of the motion of the source.

remaining constant and independent of the body's motion. But Einstein's theory invalidated the assumption.

On the basis of the theory of relativity, if the symbol m_0 represents the mass of a particle at rest with respect to an ob-

Figure 4 Albert Einstein (1879–1955). He developed the theory of relativity and revolutionized the mode of thinking about fundamental physical problems. One consequence of this theory was the extension of the concept of energy to include mass as a form of energy. Another part of the theory gives us a new insight into gravitational phenomena. He also developed the fundamental equation of the photoelectric effect and the theory of Brownian motion. (*Official U.S. Navy Photo from Acme.*)

server, then its mass m when moving with a speed of v relative to the observer is expressed by the equation

$$m = \frac{m_0}{\sqrt{1 - v^2/c^2}}$$

with c once again indicating the speed of light. One interesting conclusion to be drawn from the equation is that if a particle has a rest mass m_0, its speed v can never exceed the speed of light c. When $v = c$, $1 - v^2/c^2 = 0$ and m becomes infinite. Hence, to accelerate a particle until its speed v becomes equal to c, an infinite force—something that is not available—would be required.

In experiments with large-sized objects, or even with small particles, the speed v is generally an extremely small fraction of the speed of light. The ratio $(v/c)^2$ becomes negligible compared with unity and $m = m_0$. But when the speed v of a particle becomes an appreciable fraction of the speed of light the ratio $(v/c)^2$ is no longer negligible in comparison with unity, and mass m differs from mass m_0 of the same particle when at rest.

It is common for particles in atomic physics to have very large speeds. This becomes useful in verifying the correctness of the above equation. Experiments performed for this purpose in which electrons move at speeds comparable with the speed of light demonstrate and measure with a high degree of precision the variation of the mass of the electron with its velocity.

In one set of experiments, electrons with three separate velocities were sent through a magnetic field at right angles to their path. They traveled in circular paths of three different radii. Electrons from the same source—a radioactive substance, radium $(B + C)$—were then sent through a radial electric field between two concentric cylindrical plates (Figure 5).

By determining the precise values of the electric and magnetic fields as well as the values of the radii of the electrons' paths in these fields, we can measure with accuracy the velocities of the electrons and the ratio of the mass to charge. The ratio m_0/e is known exactly from other experimentation on slow moving electrons. If we assume the principle of conservation of charge we can obtain the ratio m/m_0—the ratio of the mass of an electron at high speed to that of an electron at rest—and compare

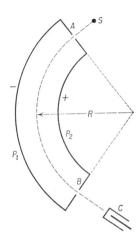

Figure 5 Electrons travel in a circular path of radius R in the electric field between the two concentric plates P_1 and P_2.

the result with what has been learned from the previous equation (page 34).

The Table below lists the results of experiments conducted in 1939 by three physicists, M. M. Rogers, A. W. McReynolds and F. T. Rogers. Note that the values these men obtained from m/m_0 agree with the values calculated from the equation above within less than 1 per cent.

Velocity of electrons in cm/sec	Ratio of electron velocity to velocity of light $= v/c$	m/m_0 from experiment	m/m_0 calculated from equation
1.8998×10^{10}	0.6337	1.298	1.293
2.0868×10^{10}	0.6961	1.404	1.393
2.2470×10^{10}	0.7496	1.507	1.511

EQUIVALENCE OF MASS AND ENERGY

Until the formulation of Einstein's special theory of relativity, one of the basic principles of physics and chemistry was the *principle of the conservation of mass*. This law stated that the mass of any substance or object remained constant under all changes of physical states and chemical composition. The principle, however, was not in accord with consequences of the theory of relativity. Einstein resolved the dilemma by postulating that *mass is a form of energy and that a mass* m *is equivalent to an amount of energy* $\mathscr{E}$. He deduced the relationship between $\mathscr{E}$ and *m* in his theory of relativity. By measuring *m* in grams or kilograms and expressing $\mathscr{E}$ in ergs or joules, the relationship between $\mathscr{E}$ and *m* was found to be

$$\mathscr{E} = mc^2.$$

The principle of conservation of energy has thus been enlarged to include mass as a form of energy. The principle of conservation of energy was originally formulated in 1847 through a positive demonstration that heat was a form of energy. Before that time, a conservation theorem existed that concerned only the mechanical forms of energy—kinetic and potential energy—for explaining transformations in systems lacking friction. Following the convincing work of Joule on the mechanical equivalent of heat, the concept of energy was extended to include heat. With the formulation of Maxwell's electromagnetic theory of light and the discovery of many forms of electromagnetic radiation, the principle of conservation of energy was expanded to include electromagnetic radiation among the forms of energy. Now, mass has become one aspect of energy along with all other forms.

Suppose you were to devise a process for converting one gram of the mass of a system into some other form of energy, say electrical energy. Using the above equation, you would get the following amount of electrical energy from the mass of one gram:

$$\mathscr{E} = 1 \text{ gm} \times (3 \times 10^{10} \text{ cm/sec})^2$$

$$\mathscr{E} = 9 \times 10^{20} \text{ ergs}$$

or $\qquad\qquad \mathscr{E} = 9 \times 10^{13} \text{ joules.}$

This is an enormous amount of energy. The fact may become more evident by changing the unit of energy from joules to kilowatt hours. Now

$$1 \text{ joule} = 1 \text{ watt} \times 1 \text{ sec};$$

hence $\qquad\quad 1 \text{ kw hr} = 1,000 \text{ watts} \times 3,600 \text{ sec,}$

or $\qquad\qquad 1 \text{ kw hr} = 36 \times 10^5 \text{ joules.}$

Moreover $\qquad\quad \mathscr{E} = \dfrac{9 \times 10^{13}}{25 \times 10^5} \text{ kw hr,}$

or $\qquad\qquad \mathscr{E} = 25 \times 10^6 \text{ kw hr.}$

Consequently, one gram of mass is equivalent to twenty-five million kw hr of electrical energy.

The conversion of mass into energy is believed to be going on continuously in the sun and the other stars. This process is the basis for the construction of nuclear reactors and nuclear weapons. The fundamental mode of converting mass into energy is through changes in the nuclear constitution of atoms. One important clue to this mode is the precise measurement of the masses of the atoms and a comparison of these values with the masses of the component particles.

POSITIVE IONS: MASS SPECTOGRAPH

The methods employed to determine the ratio of the charge to the mass of an electron can also be used to obtain the ratio of the charge to mass of the positive ions. From this ratio, it is usually easy to find the mass of an ion; in most cases, the ion's charge is equivalent to one, and sometimes two or three, electrons. The instrument designed for this purpose is known as a *mass spectrograph* or a *mass spectrometer*. The difference lies in whether a photographic plate or an electrical procedure detects the ions.

Modern mass spectrographs and spectrometers are very high precision instruments. Not only have they been used to measure atomic masses with great accuracy, but they have also been used to determine, for most of the elements, the number and relative abundance of the isotopes composing these elements. Modifications of the mass spectograph have been used also for the separation of the isotopes of elements.

The term *isotope* came about through the study of radioactive elements. Several groups of elements having identical chemical properties but different atomic weights, it was found, were formed in the process of radioactive disintegration. This meant that apparently several groups of elements occupied the same place in the periodic table. Those elements occupying the same place in the periodic table were designated by the category isotopes. Because some elements had atomic weights that differed markedly from whole numbers, it was suggested that these particular elements consisted of two or more isotopes each having a distinct atomic weight.

The search for isotopes among the nonradioactive elements was started by Thomson in 1910. The first element successfully investigated was neon. Its atomic weight 20.2 differs considerably from a whole number. By sending the positive ions formed in a gas-discharge tube through electric and magnetic fields, Thomson obtained the ratio of the charge to the mass of these ions and found that neon consists of at least two isotopes of atomic masses very close to 20 and 22. Many variations of Thomson's original method were made by subsequent investigators to improve its accuracy.

To avoid confusion, let us consider two new terms. The first, *atomic mass*, refers to the mass of an isotope of an element; it is based on a scale in which the oxygen isotope of atomic mass 16.000 is taken as the standard. This is the lightest of the three isotopes found in ordinary oxygen. The second new term, *mass number* of an isotope of an element, alludes to the whole number which is nearest to the atomic mass of the isotope.

Now there are many varieties of mass spectrographs and spectrometers in use in research and industrial laboratories. Figure 6 contains the essential parts of a mass spectrograph designed by A. J. Dempster. These parts are enclosed in a vacuum chamber. Positive ions from some source pass through the narrow slit S into a radial electric field between two cylindrical plates C_1 and C_2 of a capacitor, or electrical condenser. The ions are deflected from C_1 to C_2. Those with the appropriate

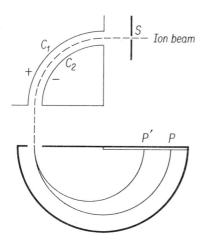

Figure 6   Dempster's mass spectrograph which uses a capacitor with cylindrical plates C_1 and C_2.

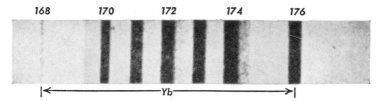

Figure 7 A photograph of the isotopes of ytterbium obtained with Dempster's mass spectrograph. The mass numbers of the isotopes can be obtained from the number scale printed above the lines. (*Reprinted from a photograph by Professor A. J. Dempster.*)

kinetic energy travel in a circular arc between the plates, their path deviating 90° from the original direction. A short distance beyond the electric field, the ions enter a uniform magnetic field which is directed at right angles to the plane of the diagram; they traverse a semicircular path and then strike the photographic plate PP' on which they are recorded.

A typical spectrogram obtained with Dempster's apparatus (Figure 7) shows the isotopes of the rare-earth element *ytterbium*. The mass number of each isotope is shown above the line formed by its ions on the photographic plate.

ATOMIC MASS AND BINDING ENERGY

One of the most important results of the precise measurements of atomic masses by mass spectrometers is that *the atomic mass of an atom is always less than the sum of the masses of the individual particles composing the atom.* Based on the equivalence of mass and energy, this means that the total energy of an atom is less than the energy of the individual particles separated from the atom. The difference between the entire energy of the separated particles and the energy of the atom itself is known as the *binding energy of the atom.* The binding energy, in effect, is that energy released in the formation of an atom and conversely, to break up an atom into its component particles, an amount of energy equivalent to its binding energy must be supplied to the atom.

Let us consider the formation of deuterium as a simple example of the meaning of binding energy. Deuterium consists of a proton and neutron in the nucleus and one electron outside

it. Its atomic mass is 2.01474 amu (atomic mass units). The
sum of the masses of deuterium's constituent particles is in
atomic mass units:

$$
\begin{aligned}
\text{mass of proton} &= 1.00760 \\
\text{mass of neutron} &= 1.00899 \\
\text{mass of electron} &= \underline{0.00055} \\
\text{sum of masses} &= 2.01714 \text{ amu.}
\end{aligned}
$$

The mass of a deuterium atom is manifestly less than the sum
of the masses of its particles by 0.00240 amu.

To appreciate the meaning of these numbers, suppose we
consider the relationship between the atomic mass unit and the
more common units of mass and energy. The physical scale of the
atomic masses is based on the designation of the number 16 as
the mass of the lightest isotope of oxygen—that is, it is written
as O^{16}. The masses of all other isotopes are measured in relation
to O^{16}, essentially atom for atom. The atomic mass of the lightest
hydrogen isotope, H^1, is thus 1.00815. A mass in grams of an
isotope numerically equal to its atomic mass is called a *gram-
atomic mass* of the isotope. One outgrowth of an hypothesis
introduced in 1811 by Avogadro is that every gram-atomic mass
of an isotope has exactly the same number of atoms. This number is designated as N_0 and is known as the *Avogadro* number.
Its present accepted value is

$$N_0 = 6.025 \times 10^{23} \text{ atoms/gram-atomic wt.}$$

The mass of any atom in grams can thus be found by dividing the atomic mass of the isotope by the Avogadro number. One
atomic mass unit—amu—is defined as one-sixteenth of the mass
of an oxygen atom of atomic mass 16. Since there are N_0 atoms
in 16 gm of oxygen, one atom has a mass of 16 gm/N_0. Hence,
1 amu, which is one-sixteenth of this, is

$$1 \text{ amu} = \frac{1 \text{ gm}}{N_0} = \frac{1 \text{ gm}}{6.025 \times 10^{23}}$$

from which

$$1 \text{ amu} = 1.66 \times 10^{-24} \text{ gm.}$$

On the basis of $\mathcal{E} = mc^2$ we find that 1 amu = 1.491×10^{-3}
erg.

Another convenient energy unit is the electron volt which is equal to the kinetic energy acquired by a particle that has a charge equivalent to that of an electron when it is accelerated in an electric field produced by a difference of potential of one volt. Since the work done by a difference of potential V acting on a charge e is Ve, then because $e = 1.60 \times 10^{-19}$ coulombs, we are able to calculate as follows:

$$1 \text{ ev} = 1.60 \times 10^{-19} \text{ coulomb} \times 1 \text{ volt}$$

$$= 1.60 \times 10^{-19} \text{ joule,}$$

or $\qquad 1 \text{ ev} = 1.60 \times 10^{-12} \text{ erg.}$

An energy of one million volts, usually abbreviated 1 Mev, forms the equation

$$1 \text{ Mev} = 1.60 \times 10^{-6} \text{ erg.}$$

It is now possible to express the atomic mass unit in Mev. Since 1 amu $= 1.49 \times 10^{-3}$ erg and 1 Mev $= 1.60 \times 10^{-6}$ erg, 1 amu $= 931.2$ Mev.

The binding energy $\mathcal{E}_B$ therefore of the deuterium atom, which has been determined as 0.00240 amu, may now be written as

$$\mathcal{E}_B = 0.00240 \times 931.2 \text{ Mev,}$$

or $\qquad \mathcal{E}_B = 2.23 \text{ Mev.}$

Another way of viewing this is that in order to separate deuterium into its component particles, an amount of energy equal to 2.23 Mev will have to be supplied to it. The binding energy of the electron in this pattern, as we shall see eventually, is only about 14 ev and thus is negligible in comparison with 2.23 Mev. We can see that this entire binding energy equals that of the two nucleons in the nucleus of the deuterium atom. Later, in the section of this book on nuclear physics, we shall examine the subject of binding energy and nuclear forces in greater detail.

4 SPECTRUM LINES AND THE BOHR ATOM

In the preceding chapters of this book, we have examined the atom and its components. Our main concerns have been with atoms, molecules, nuclei, and electrons, and with devices for studying these fundamental particles. We have learned also about mass and energy, and their roles in the atomic scheme. Now we turn attention to a closer and larger look at the *electronic structure of the atom.*

No single instrument has played a more significant part in unraveling the mysteries of modern atomic structure than the optical *spectrograph.* Originally highly specialized for purposes of basic research in physics, the spectrograph has come to be an invaluable tool commonly used in hundreds of routine industrial processes, such as testing temperature and controlling quality on the assembly line. Through it science has learned many facts about the structure of the atom and diatomic molecules—that is, molecules of two atoms.

Basically, a spectrograph performs two jobs. It decomposes light radiation into a *spectrum*—a series of colored bands arranged in order of wavelength from red, the longest visible, to violet, the shortest—and then records the action by photograph. Every spectrograph contains a prism or diffraction grating to disperse the radiation. Sometimes it has both of them. It also contains appropriate photographic equipment.

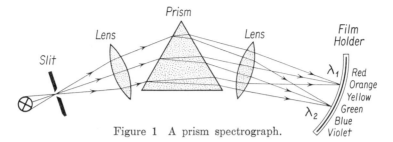

Figure 1   A prism spectrograph.

PRISM SPECTROGRAPHS

At present, there are many types of prism spectrographs in use. Most of these incorporate the basic principles of a simple prism (Figure 1). In them, light from a source passes through a slit and lens into a glass or crystalline quartz prism. Each wavelength λ emerges as a parallel beam and is brought to focus on photographic film. When developed after sufficient exposure, the film discloses a spectrum (Figure 2). The lines of the spectrum are sharply defined images of the slit, each one corresponding to a particular wavelength of light emanating from the source.

The slight curvature of the lines is typical of prism spectrographs. It results from the different angles at which the light pours through the prism. With the right kind of photographic film, the spectrum may be seen to extend beyond its visible limits. At the red end, it will then be seen to move into a region of still longer wavelengths called the *infrared,* or IR, while at the violet end, it will be seen to spill into a shorter wavelength region called the *ultraviolet,* or UV.

GRATING SPECTROGRAPHS

Diffraction gratings, which are the core of grating spectrographs, break up light into the colors of the spectrum the same

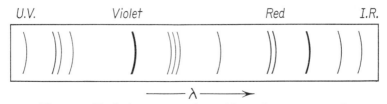

Figure 2   Typical spectrum taken with a prism spectrograph.

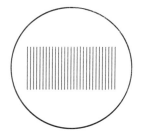

Figure 3   Diffraction grating.

way a prism spectrograph does but with greater uniformity. They are composed (Figure 3) of thousands of closely spaced, parallel lines, ruled on mirrored surfaces. Some of these surfaces are plane and others concave. The diffraction gratings in these spectrographs are ruled on a highly reflective surface.

In a spectrograph containing a plane reflection grating, the light enters through a slit at the side of the instrument (Figure 4). It is then reflected by a small reflecting prism and refracted into a parallel beam by the lens. After diffraction takes place at the grating, a set of parallel rays for each wavelength of the original light is brought to focus on the photographic film at a different place. When a concave grating is used the lens can be eliminated.

The chief advantage of the grating spectrograph over the prism spectrograph is the uniform dispersion it produces along the photographic film. This makes it easier to determine wavelengths from measurement of the individual line images.

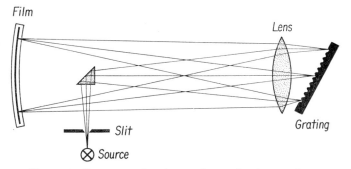

Figure 4   Spectrograph using a plane reflection grating.

KINDS OF SPECTRA

Studies of many spectra produced by light from all types of sources have led to the establishment of two general classes: *continuous spectra* and *line spectra*.

We find a spectrum to be a continuous band when any solid is heated to incandescence—white heat—and its light is examined with a spectroscope. The visible spectrum appears to terminate at the red on one side and the violet on the other. But a photograph made with a spectrograph shows the light stretching into the infrared at one end and the ultraviolet at the other. If the intensity of this light is plotted on a graph (Figure 5), a peak may be observed at some particular wavelength. But if the temperature of the source is raised, the intensity increases at all wavelengths and the peak shifts to the shorter ones—toward the ultraviolet. When, however, the temperature is lowered, the intensity falls off at every wavelength and the peak moves to the higher—or infrared—wavelengths.

This shift in the peak is known as *Wien's Displacement Law*. It is expressed by the equation

$$C = \lambda_{\max}\, T$$

in which $\lambda_{\max}$ represents the peak wavelength and T the corre-

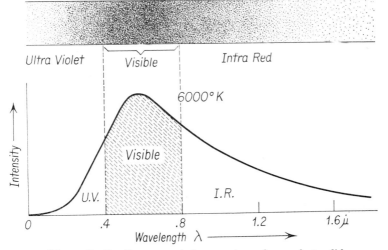

Figure 5 Continuous omission spectrum from a hot solid.

sponding temperature. The constant C has the value of 2.897×10^{-3} meters $^{\circ}K$.

Every time an electrical discharge is sent through a gas, the atoms and molecules give off discrete wavelengths of light peculiar to the particular atomic particles of the gas. When this light is exposed to spectrographic examination, it is found to be composed of a set of lines (Figure 6). Each line is an image of the spectrograph slit produced for each wavelength of light. The term *line spectrum* derives its name, therefore, from the images, while each individual line corresponds to a frequency of the atom or molecule.

The line spectrum of most of the known chemical elements is complex and appears to be a random array of wavelengths without any apparent order. The spectra of some elements, however, reveal one or more regular patterns of lines called *spectral series*. These series arise from elements in the first two columns of the periodic table (page 3). Although the line spectra of most elements contain hundreds of lines and seem to be extremely intricate, the frequencies they emit have been found to supply important information concerning the atomic energy states. It is through a study of these states that we obtain concrete knowledge of the electronic structure of the elements.

When white light from a hot solid passes through the gas of the chemical elements, certain of its frequencies are absorbed by the gas's atoms and molecules. The evidence of this absorption consists of the dark lines that appear in the white light spectrum. It corresponds exactly with some of the natural frequencies those same atoms and molecules would emit if heated to incandescence.

THE HYDROGEN SPECTRUM

The spectrum lines of hydrogen (Figure 6) can be observed in the sun and in thousands of stars as absorption lines. Because of this prominence, many of the early scientists sought in vain for a plausible explanation of their wavelengths. In 1885, Balmer was the first to achieve any success in the search. He expressed his findings in the following simple equation which has come to be known as *Balmer's Formula*:

$$\lambda_n = B \frac{n^2}{n^2 - m^2}.$$

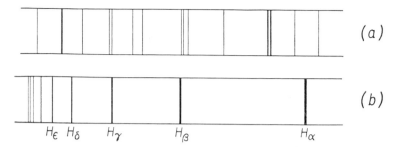

Figure 6 Drawings of typical line spectra. (*a*) Complex spectra as produced by an element like iron. (*b*) Spectral line series as produced by an element like hydrogen.

In this equation, λ_n symbolizes the wavelength of any of the lines, B the constant, and n and m whole numbers. The value of B is 3645.6 A (Angstrom units; that is, a unit of length called the angstrom and equal to 0.00000001 cm).

By inserting the values 2 and 3 for m and n respectively in Balmer's Formula, the wavelength λ equals 6562.08 A. This agrees exactly with the measured wavelength of the hydrogen red line H_α. By using $m = 2$ and $n = 4$ instead, the wavelength equals 4860.80 A, the measured wavelength of the hydrogen green line H_β.

Similar efforts to fit the spectral series of other elements to a simple formula also have been successful. The principal equation for all these series was developed by Rydberg primarily and is known as the *Rydberg Formula*. It is expressed this way:

$$\nu_n = \nu_\infty - R/(n - \Lambda)^2.$$

This formula covers the frequencies ν_n of almost every series of spectral lines in all the elements. For each the three constants ν_∞, R and A have to be evaluated. Curiously, R has the same value for all, while the others, ν_∞ and A, differ from series to series and element to element.

THE THOMSON ATOM

Present-day concepts of atomic structure have been influenced by many previous studies. One of the earliest to bear directly on the subject was undertaken in 1912 by J. J. Thomson. He proposed what has been called many times the "plum pud-

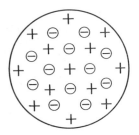

Figure 7   Diagram of the Thomson (plum pudding) model of the atom.

ding" structure of the atom (Figure 7). Thomson suggested that the bulk of an atom was composed of a solid sphere of positive charge impregnated by tiny electrons in concentric rings, or shells.

His reasoning was based on knowledge obtained from studies of radioactivity, cathode rays, and positive rays. These investigations showed that two kinds of charged atomic particles existed, those of positive and those of negative charge. The positively charged particles carry practically all the mass and vary from one element to another, whereas the negatively charged particles are all alike and are thousands of times lighter in weight. Drawing on these facts and the law governing the attraction and repulsion of charges, Thomson devised his structure of the atom.

Thomson's type of structure can be shown to be mathematically sound, but its principal value has been the guidance it has provided toward reaching our current views of atomic structure.

THE BOHR ATOM

A year after Thomson developed his structure for the atom, a theory of the hydrogen atom advanced by Niels Bohr marked the dawn of a new era in atomic physics. Bohr proposed not only a structure for the atom that satisfactorily explained the Balmer Formula for hydrogen spectrum lines, but a principle upon which to build the electron structure of all atoms and molecules.

As we have seen, the hydrogen atom consists of a positively charged nucleus and a single negatively charged electron (Figure 9). The electron orbits the nucleus much the same as a planet like the earth moves around the sun. Because the nucleus has 1840 times the mass of the electron, it may be thought of as remaining more or less stationary.

Figure 8 Niels Bohr. Made outstanding contributions to the modern theory of the nuclear structure of the atom, both for electronic processes and nuclear processes. (*Courtesy of the American Institute of Physics.*)

To move in a circular path, the electron has to have a centripetal force—a force pulling it toward the center—exerted upon it. This force is expressed by the equation

$$F = m\frac{v^2}{r}.$$

It is the electrostatic attractive force exerted on the electron by the nucleus. It may be written in terms of the law propounded by the French physicist Charles Augustin de Coulomb and named

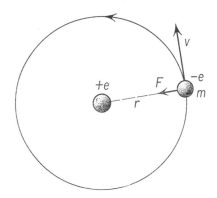

Figure 9 Orbital model of the hydrogen atom according to the Bohr theory.

Coulomb's Law. Coulomb's law deals with the electrostatic attraction and repulsion of charges, and is given as

$$F = \frac{ee}{r^2}.$$

From this, we see that

$$m\frac{v^2}{r} = \frac{ee}{r^2}.$$

Bohr proposed a restriction on the orbiting electron, a restriction basic to the quantum theory. This confines the electron to those orbits in which the angular momentum equals a whole number multiplied by a constant. Put into an equation, this may be expressed as

$$mvr = nh/2\pi.$$

The whole number *n* represents the *principal quantum number* ($n = 1, 2, 3, 4$, etc.). The constant *h* is Planck's constant.

When the equations governing the force exerted on the orbital electron and the quantum restriction are combined, Bohr found that the energies $\mathcal{E}$ of the electron in the various permitted orbits may be given by

$$\mathcal{E} = -\frac{2\pi^2 m e^4}{n^2 h^2}$$

and the radii of the corresponding orbits may be given by

$$r = \frac{h^2}{4\pi^2 m e^2} n^2.$$

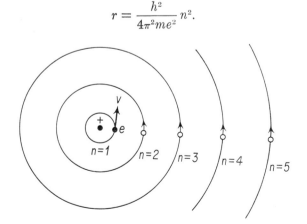

Figure 10   Diagram of the allowed orbits for the single electron in the hydrogen atom.

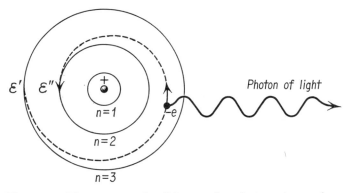

Figure 11   The atom emits light as the electron jumps from one quantized orbit to another.

When the known values of the electronic charge e and mass m are inserted, along with Planck's constant h, the orbits shown in Figure 10 are obtained. The electron normally travels the innermost orbit—$n = 1$. But it may be bumped, as we know, to one of the other authenticated orbits by sufficiently severe collisions between normal atoms.

In Bohr's opinion, an atom with its electron in one of the outer orbits will emit light as the electron jumps back to an inner orbit (Figure 11). To have lifted the electron to an outer orbit in the first place took an expenditure of energy. In returning to the innermost orbit, therefore, there is a liberation of energy, and this takes the form of a light wave, or quantum. As expressed by Bohr

$$\mathcal{E}_i - \mathcal{E}_f = h\nu.$$

The symbols $\mathcal{E}_i$ and $\mathcal{E}_F$ represent the energies of the outer and final orbits, respectively, h is the Planck constant and ν is the frequency of the light emitted. The energy $h\nu$ is called a *quantum*.

ELECTRON TRANSITIONS

When an electron in a hydrogen atom is pushed from its innermost orbit, called its normal state, into any of the allowable outer orbits, the atom is said to be *excited*. If the outer orbit is some other one than $n = 2$, the return of the electron to the normal

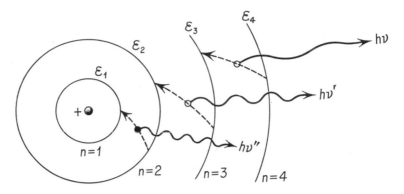

Figure 12   The electron returning to its normal state may emit several light quanta.

state may occur with the emission of several different light quanta (Figure 12). An electron excited to the fourth orbit out may return to the normal state by jumping to orbit $\mathcal{E}_3$, then to orbit $\mathcal{E}_2$, and finally to $\mathcal{E}_1$, with the emission of three light waves of different frequencies. It could also skip from $\mathcal{E}_4$ to $\mathcal{E}_2$ and then to $\mathcal{E}_1$, or from $\mathcal{E}_4$ to $\mathcal{E}_3$ and then to $\mathcal{E}_1$, or from $\mathcal{E}_4$ to $\mathcal{E}_1$ directly. In other words, six different ways of transition are possible, giving rise to six different frequencies of light.

With millions of hydrogen atoms in an electrical discharge, the large number of those excited gives rise to all possible transitions of this kind. In their several spectra, we may observe the exact frequencies and wavelengths calculated from Bohr's equations.

The Balmer hydrogen series we considered earlier in the chapter results from those transitions that end on the second orbit. The red line H_α is an outgrowth of the transition $\mathcal{E}_3$ to $\mathcal{E}_2$, the green line H_β a consequence of the transition $\mathcal{E}_4$ to $\mathcal{E}_2$, etc.

Transitions from the outer orbits ending on the innermost produce high frequencies of light. These radiations can be observed in the ultraviolet spectrum of hydrogen and the exact wavelengths determined by Bohr's equations. They are called the *Lyman Series* after the name of the man who discovered them. Another series of hydrogen lines created by transitions terminating on the orbit $n = 3$, may be found in the infrared region of the spectrum. These radiation lines are called the *Paschen Series* in honor of their discoverer.

ELLIPTICAL ORBITS

Not long after the announcement of the Bohr theory of hydrogen, an extension of the orbital model was proposed by Arnold Sommerfeld. Although this did not lead to any further lines in the hydrogen spectrum, it gave the electrons greater freedom by permitting them to move in elliptical as well as circular orbits (Figure 13). Sommerfeld's theory calls for two quantum numbers, the principal quantum number n introduced by Bohr, and a new one k called the *azimuthal quantum number*. The latter gets its name from the clockwise distance in degrees from a fixed point. While both n and k are whole numbers, the value of k never may be larger than n.

The related values are

$n = 1$	$n = 2$	$n = 2$	$n = 3$	$n = 3$	$n = 3$
$k = 1$	$k = 1$	$k = 2$	$k = 1$	$k = 2$	$k = 3$
$1\,s$	$2\,s$	$2\,p$	$3\,s$	$3\,p$	$3\,d$

The designations s, p, d, etc., refer to the values of $k = 1, 2, 3$, etc., respectively, and constitute a shorthand notation commonly used by atomic physicists. One can note from these relationships that for each value of n there are n allowable orbits.

Sommerfeld demonstrated that at first approximation all orbits with the same principal quantum number have the same energy and that transitions from one orbit to another produce

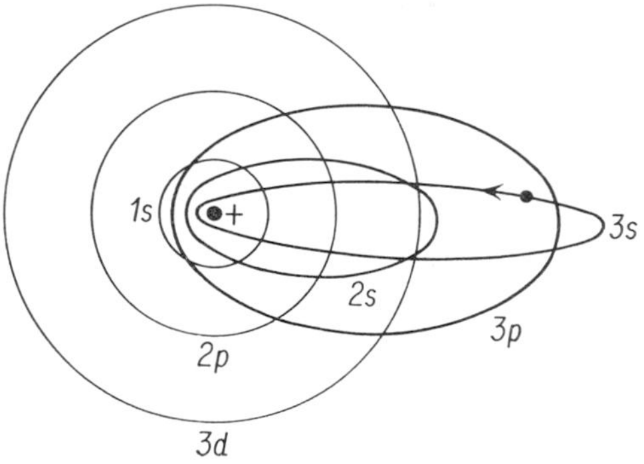

Figure 13 Circular and elliptical orbits for the single electron in hydrogen.

the same spectrum lines as the Bohr theory. But now transitions between orbits are somewhat restricted and limited to those changes for which

$$\Delta k = +1 \text{ or } -1.$$

In other words, k must change by one unit only, thereby prohibiting transitions such as $3s$ to $3d$, $2s$, or $1s$.

Although the Bohr-Sommerfeld theory leads to the correct energy equations for the hydrogen atom and explains the spectrum that may be seen with a great degree of precision, we know now that its orbital pattern is not wholly accurate and that, furthermore, the quantum number k must be reduced by 1. In the new wave-mechanics concepts we will find it convenient to replace k by the orbital quantum number l and to accept this series of relationships:

$n = 1$	$n = 2$	$n = 2$	$n = 3$	$n = 3$	$n = 3$
$l = 0$	$l = 0$	$l = 1$	$l = 0$	$l = 1$	$l = 2$
$1s$	$1s$	$2p$	$3s$	$3p$	$3d$

For higher values of l, the following symbols are used:

$$l = 0 \quad 1 \quad 2 \quad 3 \quad 4 \quad 5 \ldots$$
$$ s \quad p \quad d \quad f \quad g \quad h \ldots$$

We therefore speak of an electron in an orbit with $n = 3$ and $l = 1$, as a $3p$ electron; $n = 3$ and $l = 2$ as a $3d$ electron, etc.

5 ENERGY LEVELS AND THE SPINNING ELECTRON

ENERGY LEVELS OF HYDROGEN

It is customary to visualize electrons as moving about in orbits whose size and shape depend on two quantum numbers, the principal quantum number n and the orbital quantum number l. We noted in the preceding chapter how these two quanta restrict the motion of an electron in an atom to certain orbits. Although this mental image we commonly draw is not entirely accurate, we do know that the equations about energy based on a theory covering such orbiting patterns are correct. They are correct because they agree to a high degree of precision with what we can observe about the frequencies of spectrum lines.

The energy $\mathcal{E}$ of the electron in any of the allowable orbits of hydrogen is given by the Bohr equation (page 50). These energies, expressed in ergs, are usually divided by Planck's constant h and the speed of light c. The energy then becomes expressed as T in units called *reciprocal centimeters*, or *wave numbers*, which are symbolized by cm⁻¹.

Combining all the constants except the quantum number n into a single one, the Bohr equation may be simplified into

$$T = R/n^2$$

with R representing the Rydberg constant, and T the *term value*. The numerical value of R is 109737 cm⁻¹.

Using Bohr's equation for the emission of light, $\mathcal{E}_i - \mathcal{E}_f = h\nu$,

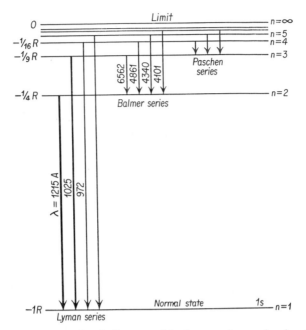

Figure 1   Energy level diagram of hydrogen atoms, showing the electron transitions giving rise to the observed series of spectrum lines.

we may now use term values R/n^2 in place of energies $\mathscr{E}$, and wavelengths λ in place of frequencies ν, and write

$$\frac{1}{\lambda} = \frac{R}{n^2_i} - \frac{R}{n^2_f}$$

where λ is measured in centimeters.

Rather than draw a series of orbits to depict the allowable states of the atom, suppose we draw an energy graph which is of far greater meaning. Figure 1 contains the graph for hydrogen and is called an *Energy Level Diagram*. The zero level at the top represents the hydrogen atom with its one and only electron removed from the atom. The lowest horizontal line refers to the atom with its electron in its innermost allowable state, $n = 1$, and is called the *normal state*, or the *ground state*. The remaining horizontal lines correspond to the other permissible orbits and are called the *excited states*.

Vertical arrows pointing downward indicate the emission of

light by the hydrogen atoms. When, for example, the electron slips from orbital state $n = 3$ to orbital state $n = 2$, the light emitted by the atom has a wavelength of 6562 A; this may be observed as the red line in the Balmer series of the hydrogen atom.

Since the term values—R, $1/4$ R, $1/9$ R, $1/16$ R, etc.—are plotted in the energy level diagram, the lengths of the arrows are directly proportional to the frequencies of the radiated light. The long arrows symbolize the highest frequencies of the Lyman series in the short wavelength region—the ultraviolet spectrum. The shorter arrows indicate the lower frequencies of the Paschen series in the long wavelength region—the infrared spectrum.

THE BOHR-STONER SCHEME

In the years following Bohr's formulation of a theory of the hydrogen atom (1913), many attempts were made to extend the Bohr theory to other kinds of atoms. As guides for such theorizing several important experimental observations proved useful:

First, there was the periodic table which listed the elements in order of their atomic weights.

Second, there were the spectra of most of the elements which revealed well-defined series of lines similar to hydrogen.

Third, Rydberg had noted that the atomic numbers of inert gases—helium, neon, argon, krypton, xenon, and radon—were based on a formula of this kind:

$$Z = 2(1^2 + 2^2 + 2^2 + 3^2 + 3^2 + 4^2);$$

that is, they are 2, 10, 18, 36, 54, and 86 respectively. These are said to be "magic numbers."

Fourth, Rutherford's scattering experiments, performed with alpha particles from radioactive elements, showed that the charge of a nucleus was equal to approximately one-half the atomic weight.

Fifth, there was Thomson's "plum pudding" proposal for the electron shell model of the atom.

With all these criteria in mind, Bohr suggested that each element in its turn, starting with hydrogen, could be built up by adding one more positive charge to the nucleus and one more orbiting electron. Stoner proposed a similar stone-building scheme but assigned different numbers of electrons to the subshells. Today we know exactly what the order is for most of the elements in the periodic table (page 3).

The numbers of the elements in each of the periods of the periodic table hold the clue to the major electron shells. They are the total number of electrons required to complete, or close, any shell. They are represented by $2n^2$, n signifying the principal quantum number. Thus, the total number of electrons in the K-shell is 2 because $n = 1$; the L-shell is 8, with n equaling 2; the M-shell ($n = 3$) is 18, and the N-shell ($n = 4$) is 32.

Within each shell are the following subshells:

K–shell	L–shell		M–shell			N–shell			
$n = 1$	$n = 2$		$n = 3$			$n = 4$			
$l = 0$	$l = 0$	$l = 1$	$l = 0$	$l = 1$	$l = 2$	$l = 0$	$l = 1$	$l = 2$	$l = 3$
$1s$	$2s$	$2p$	$3s$	$3p$	$3d$	$4s$	$4p$	$4d$	$4f$
(2)	(2)	(6)	(2)	(6)	(10)	(2)	(6)	(10)	(14)

The total number of electrons allowable in any subshell is

$$2(2l + 1).$$

For want of a better picture, we may draw atoms with their electron orbits (Figure 2). The right-hand diagram is the easier

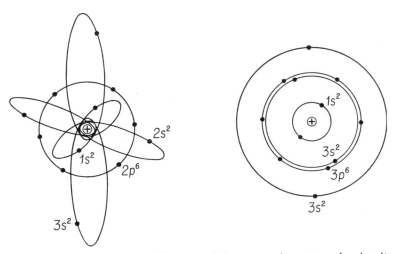

Figure 2   Two different diagrams of the magnesium atom showing its twelve electrons in the shells and subshells.

Distribution of Electrons in the Atoms

X-Ray Notation		K	L		M			N			
Quantum Numbers n, l		1,0	2,0	2,1	3,0	3,1	3,2	4,0	4,1	4,2	4,3
Element	Atomic Number Z										
H	1	1									
He	2	2									
Li	3	2	1								
Be	4	2	2								
B	5	2	2	1							
C	6	2	2	2							
N	7	2	2	3							
O	8	2	2	4							
F	9	2	2	5							
Ne	10	2	2	6							
Na	11		Neon Configuration 10 electron core		1						
Mg	12				2						
Al	13				2	1					
Si	14				2	2					
P	15				2	3					
S	16				2	4					
Cl	17				2	5					
A	18				2	6					
K	19		Argon Configuration 18 electron core					1			
Ca	20							2			
Sc	21						1	2			
Ti	22						2	2			
V	23						3	2			
Cr	24						5	1			
Mn	25						5	2			
Fe	26						6	2			
Co	27						7	2			
Ni	28						8	2			
Cu	29						10	1			
Zn	30						10	2			
Ga	31						10	2	1		
Ge	32						10	2	2		
As	33						10	2	3		
Se	34						10	2	4		
Br	35						10	2	5		
Kr	36						10	2	6		

X-Ray Notation		K L M	N			O			P			Q	
Quantum Numbers n,l		1 2 3	4,0 4,1	4,2	4,3	5,0	5,1	5,2	6,0	6,1	6,2	7,0	7,1
Element	Atomic Number Z												
Rb	37	Krypton Configuration 36 electron core				1							
Sr	38					2							
Y	39			1		2							
Zr	40			2		2							
Nb	41			4		1							
Mo	42			5		1							
Ma	43			6		1							
Ru	44			7		1							
Rh	45			8		1							
Pd	46			10									
Ag	47	Palladium Configuration 46 electron core				1							
Cd	48					2							
In	49					2	1						
Sn	50					2	2						
Sb	51					2	3						
Te	52					2	4						
I	53					2	5						
Xe	54					2	6						
Cs	55	Xenon Configuration 54 electron core							1				
Ba	56								2				
La	57	Shells 1,0 to 4,2 contain 46 electrons				2	6	1	2				
Ce	58				1	2	6	1	2				
Pr	59				2	2	6	1	2				
Nd	60				3	2	6	1	2				
Pm	61				4	2	6	1	2				
Sm	62				5	2	6	1	2				
Eu	63				6	2	6	1	2				
Gd	64				7	2	6	1	2				
Tb	65				8	2	6	1	2				
Dy	66				9	2	6	1	2				
Ho	67				10	2	6	1	2				
Er	68				11	2	6	1	2				
Tm	69				13	2	6	0	2				
Yb	70				14	2	6	C	2				
Lu	71				14	2	6	1	2				

X-Ray Notation		K L M N	O			P			Q	
Quantum Numbers n, l		1 2 3 4	5,0 5,1	5,2	5,3	6,0	6,1	6,2	7,0	7,1
Element	Atomic Number Z									
Hf	72			2		2				
Ta	73			3		2				
W	74			4		2				
Re	75			5		2				
Os	76			6		2				
Ir	77			7		2				
Pt	78	Shells		9		1				
Au	79	1,0 to 5,1		10		1				
Hg	80	contain		10		2				
Tl	81	68 electrons		10		2	1			
Pb	82			10		2	2			
Bi	83			10		2	3			
Po	84			10		2	4			
At	85			10		2	5			
Rn	86			10		2	6			
Fr	87	Radon Configuration							1	
Ra	88	80 electron core							2	
Ac	89					2	6	1	2	
Th	90				1	2	6	1	2	
Pa	91				2	2	6	1	2	
U	92				3	2	6	1	2	
Np	93				4	2	6	1	2	
Pu	94				5	2	6	1	2	
Am	95				6	2	6	1	2	
Cm	96				7	2	6	1	2	
Bk	97				8	2	6	1	2	
Cf	98				9	2	6	1	2	
E	99				10	2	6	1	2	
Fm	100				11	2	6	1	2	
Mv	101				12	2	6	1	2	

to complete, while the left-hand diagram provides a mental image of penetrating and nonpenetrating orbits.

PENETRATING ORBITS

About ten years after the Bohr-Sommerfeld orbital theory of hydrogen was developed and the hydrogen spectrum seemed to be completely explained, a new theory called *quantum mechanics* was evolved by Schroedinger. While the newer quantum mechanics retained the quantum numbers needed to form the various shells and subshells found to exist through experiments, the orbital picture still had to be recognized as a fiction. For both simplicity and brevity, nevertheless, the orbital model is still used widely whenever diagrams are required to help understand the phenomena we observe (Figure 3).

Although the azimuthal quantum number k (page 53) of the Bohr-Sommerfeld theory was reduced by one to become the orbital quantum number l, we may write the *angular momentum* of an electron orbit as the following equation:

$$l^* = \sqrt{l(l+1)}\ \frac{h}{2\pi}$$

where for $\qquad\qquad l = 0\ \ 1\ \ 2\ \ 3\ \ 4 \text{ --- --- ---,}$
we write $\qquad\qquad s\ \ p\ \ d\ \ f\ \ g \text{ --- --- ---.}$

On the orbital model this presents some problems because all s-orbits—those for which $l = 0$—have zero, or no, angular

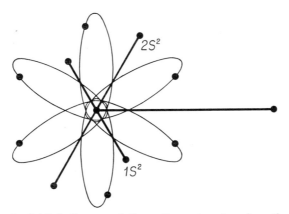

Figure 3   Orbital diagram of the sodium atom based partly on quantum mechanics.

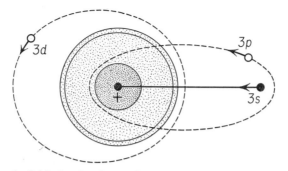

Figure 4 Orbitals of valence electron in sodium atom showing penetrating orbits 3s and 3p, and nonpenetrating orbit 3d.

momentum. In other words, the Bohr-Sommerfeld ellipses for orbits in these states have a minor axis of zero so that the orbit becomes a straight line with the nucleus located at one end. All other orbits become ellipses with both minor and major axes.

The alkali metals—lithium, sodium, potassium, rubidium, cesium, and francium—all contain one *valence* electron. This means they each have one electron to share with other elements in chemical bonding. Physically it means that all their electrons but one, for each metal, form closed subshells and are tightly bound to the nucleus.

Consider, for example, the sodium atom, atomic number 11 (Figure 4). The closed subshells of ten electrons may be visualized as forming a spherical electron cloud that shields the nucleus from the outer electron, 3s. When 3s is outside this *core*, the effective nuclear charge will approximate +e. When, however, it penetrates close to the nucleus, the entire charge of +11e becomes effective. The average attracting force throughout the entire orbit will be greater, therefore, than +e.

If the valence electron of sodium is forced to move in orbit 3d, it will not penetrate the electron core and will remain instead in the electric field of an effective nuclear charge of +e. This qualitative treatment of penetrating and nonpenetrating orbits leads to greater understanding of the energy level diagrams of atoms such as sodium. In these atoms, the valence electron jumps among excited states and to the normal state. In so doing, it gives rise to series of spectrum lines observable through experiment.

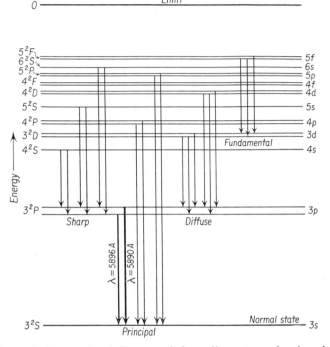

Figure 5   Energy level diagram of the sodium atom, showing electron transitions.

ENERGY LEVEL DIAGRAMS

When energy level diagrams are made for the alkaline earth elements, many similarities among them stand out. One of these is that the normal state, or ground level, is a single level and that many of the other levels are double. The first excited state, moreover, is a doublet P-level (Figure 5). These are followed by ^2S, ^2P, ^2D, and ^2F levels, coming closer and closer to zero energy as a limit.

The level designations at the right signify the quantum numbers—n and l—of the valence electron. Those at the left are term designations. The exponent 2 signifies that the level belongs to the doublet set.

As in hydrogen, electron transitions from one orbit to another are indicated by vertical arrows. Transitions from ^2P-levels ending on the normal state, ^2S, produce the principal series of spectrum lines seen in the sodium spectrum. The first pair of lines corresponds to the strong yellow doublet that characterizes the color of all sodium lamps.

The sharp series of lines observed in the sodium spectrum result from transitions beginning on ^2S-levels and ending on the first excited state, $3\ ^2P$. Note also that the diffuse series start on ^2D-levels, end on the $3\ ^2P$-levels, and give rise to three closely spaced spectrum lines for each series number.

THE SPINNING ELECTRON

In 1925, Uhlenbeck and Goudsmit sought to account for the doublet structure of the energy levels in the alkali metals by proposing the concept of a spinning electron. We now know that all electrons spin, whether they are free, or bound to atoms in solids, liquids, or gases. In spinning, they have an angular momentum which is expressed by the equation

$$s^* = \sqrt{s(s+1)}\ \frac{h}{2\pi}.$$

The quantum number s here has only a single value, $1/2$. The orbital image of the atom, therefore, takes on an even closer resemblance to planetary motion (Figure 6).

Since the quantum mechanics requires angular momentum to be *quantized*—that is, given definite prescribed values of a unit $h/2\pi$—the spin and orbit axes of rotation have to take on fixed positions, one with the other. This *space quantization* is best represented by vector diagrams employing the right-hand rule developed in mechanics (Figure 7). The vector resulting from spin angular momentum s^* and orbital angular momentum l^* is

Figure 6 The spinning electron and its orbital motion are similar to planetary motion.

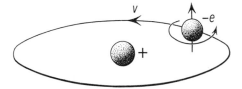

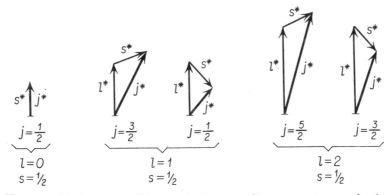

Figure 7   Electron spin-orbit quantization according to quantum mechanics.

designated by j^* which may be derived from the following equation:

$$j^* = \sqrt{j\,(j+1)}\,\frac{h}{2\pi}$$

with j equal to $1/2, 3/2, 5/2, 7/2. \ldots$

This number j, the *inner quantum number*, it will be seen from the vector diagrams, has two values for all values of l except $l = 0$. These correspond to the doubling of all the energy levels except the S-levels in atoms with but one valence electron. In all atoms, the total angular momentum of each completed shell and subshell is nonexistent; that is, it is zero.

THE BOHR MAGNETON

An electron in orbit has, in addition to angular momentum l^*, a magnetic moment μ_l. Because the electron is negatively charged, it creates a symmetrical magnetic field around the axis. This field is much the same as the magnetic field of a small bar magnet with north and south poles. For a straight bar magnet with two poles, each of a strength M and spacing l, the magnetic moment is expressed as

$$\mu = Ml.$$

The magnetic moment of a current loop such as an electron in its orbit, on the other hand, is written as

$$\mu_l = \sqrt{l(l+1)}\left(\frac{h}{2\pi} \times \frac{e}{2m}\right).$$

If we call all the terms inside the parenthesis μ_1 and insert the known values of the atomic constants h, e, and m, we may compute the value of μ_1 as 9.27×10^{-27} ergs/gauss. This μ_1 is used in studies of atomic structure and in honor of Niels Bohr is called the *Bohr magneton*.

Magnetic moment is represented at times by μ_l because it is a vector quantity (Figure 8). Note that the angular momentum l^*, which is sometimes called the *mechanical moment*, is opposite in direction to the magnetic moment.

Just as a mechanical top precesses—rotates—around an axis when it spins in a gravitational field, so does an electron orbit rotate in similar circumstances. Figure 9 compares these two motions. Because of the earth's gravitational field, there is a downward force that acts through the top's center of mass and an equal but opposite force exerted by the pivot P. This creates a *torque*—that is, a combination of forces that tends to produce a twisting or rotating motion—that adds another angular momentum around a horizontal axis. Combined with the spin angular momentum, $I\omega$ along the top's axis this causes a rotation, or *precession*.

The magnetic moment μ_l of the electron orbit in a magnetic field B experiences a torque $\mu_l B$ that tries to pull it parallel to

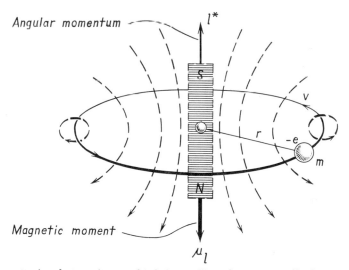

Figure 8   An electron in an orbit behaves like a bar magnet dipole moment.

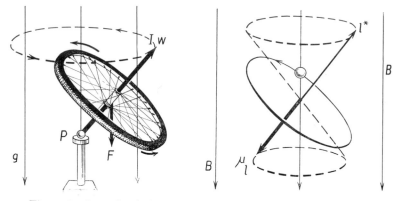

Figure 9   A mechanical top precessing in a uniform gravitational field
g is analogous to an electron orbit precessing in a uniform magnetic field.

the field. This torque produces an angular momentum about a
horizontal axis; when combined with the angular momentum l^*
along the orbital axis, it gives rise to a similar precession.
Whereas the torque results from a magnetic interaction, the precession is mechanical. The angular velocity o of the precession
around the direction of the field is represented by

$$o = \frac{\mu_l}{l^*} B .$$

This motion is called the *Larmor precession*.

Since all electrons, those free in space as well as those bound
to an atom, have a spin angular momentum s^*, they also have a
spin magnetic moment μ_s. Peculiarly enough, the spinning electron with the spin angular moment quantum number $s = 1/2$ has
a magnetic moment of one Bohr magneton. Here again the magnetic moment μ_s (Figure 10) is opposite in direction to the mechanical moment s^*.

A spinning electron may be expected to precess around the
field direction the same way an orbital electron precesses in a
magnetic field.

SPIN-ORBIT INTERACTION

In the foregoing section we have seen that the spin and
orbiting motions of a bound electron create separate magnetic

fields (Figures 8 and 10). Although these fields may be expected to react upon each other, the quantum conditions applying to angular momentum require that the value of j^* be derived from l^* and s^* (Figure 7).

The magnetic field at the electron orbit, it will be observed (Figure 8), is zero because of the orbital motion of the electron. The field lines grow more circular as they near the orbit and ultimately become zero. But there is an effective magnetic field at the electron. This field results from the presence of a positively charged nucleus. If we imagine that we are riding around the orbit with the electron, we would see the positively charged nucleus moving around us in an orbit of the same size. Put another way, the magnetic field B at the spinning electron is the same as that of a positive charge moving around the electron in an orbit (Figure 11).

The spinning electron with its magnetic moment μ_s tries to precess around B, while μ_l, which is parallel to B, attempts to precess around the spin field. As a result, all moments precess around j^* (Figure 12).

Except for s-electron orbits in which $l = 0$, there are two possible directions for spin s^* and orbit l^* to form j^*. These two orientations produce two closely spaced energy levels. From the energy level diagrams of atoms containing one valence electron, we find the level with the lower of the two j-values lying deeper

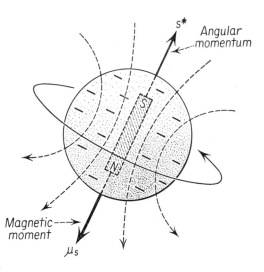

Figure 10 Because of its negative charge a spinning electron has a magnetic dipole moment.

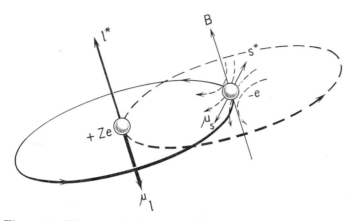

Figure 11   Diagram showing the orbital and spin angular moments above, and magnetic moments below.

than the other. Thus, for a p-electron with $l = 1$, the two energy states allowable, $j = 1/2$ and $j = 3/2$, will have slightly different energies, the level $j = 1/2$ lying deeper than the level $j = 3/2$. In the same manner, the level $j = 3/2$ will lie below the level $j = 5/2$ for a d-electron in which $l = 2$.

We can now understand the reason for this. Figure 11 shows

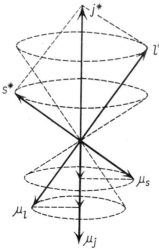

Figure 12   The electron spin and orbit moments precess around their resultant angular momentum j^*.

that the position of the electron spin axis will be most stable when it is most nearly parallel to the orbital field B. To roll the electron axis over from allowable position $j = l - 1/2$ to allowable position $j = l + 3/2$ requires exerting a torque through an angle θ and hence work. For this reason, the doublet state, $j = l - 1/2$, should lie deepest in the diagram.

Figure 13 depicts doublet levels in their relative positions labeled with their proper designations. It will be noted that each capital letter signifies the orbital l-value and the subscripts the j-values.

SELECTION RULES

The arrows in Figure 13 signify the transitions between energy levels in an atom. These transitions produce emissions of light and correspond to spectrum lines observed. The dotted arrows indicate *forbidden lines*. They show where transitions

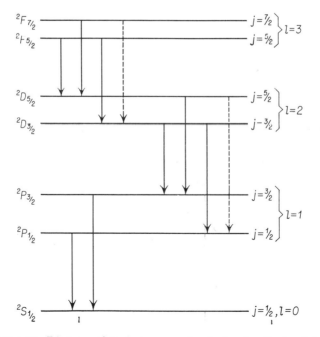

Figure 13   Diagram of typical energy levels showing the level designations and quantum numbers as well as allowed transitions.

cannot take place. In other words, we may say that selection rules operate within the atom.

The first selection rule covers the orbital quantum number and stipulates that in any transition l may change by one—and *only* one—unit. Transitions may occur from $l = 3$ to $l = 2$, $l = 2$ to $l = 1$, $l = 1$ to $l = 0$, $l = 0$ to $l = 1$, $l = 1$ to $l = 2$, etc. But they are forbidden from $l = 3$ to $l = 1$, $l = 2$ to $l = 0$, etc. This may be expressed by the formula

$$\triangle l = +1, \text{ or } -1.$$

The second rule deals with the inner quantum number and may be written

$$\triangle j = +1, 0, \text{ or } -1.$$

From the diagram, we can see that the transitions $j = 7/2$ to $j = 3/2$, etc., are forbidden.

THE ZEEMAN EFFECT

When a source of light is placed between the poles of a strong electromagnet, and the light is examined with a spectrograph, many of the spectrum lines are seen to broaden appreciably, while others develop into symmetrical line patterns. This effect was first noted by Zeeman in 1896 and partially explained in terms of atomic structure the following year by Hendrik Lorentz. Because of the many different line patterns in any single spectrum and the important information that interpretation of each pattern yields about the structure of the particular atoms emitting the light, we shall turn our attention to this subject for the moment.

Figure 14 contains a cross-section diagram of the apparatus for observing the *Zeeman effect*. The light from the source S passing through a small hole in the right-hand pole piece enters the slit of the spectrograph. This light, which travels along the direction of the magnetic induction B, is called the *longitudinal Zeeman effect*. If the light is seen from a direction perpendicular to B, the spectrum line pattern that is observed is called the *transverse Zeeman effect*.

The bottom-most diagram and the one at the far right show typical patterns for an individual spectrum line. Some of the light

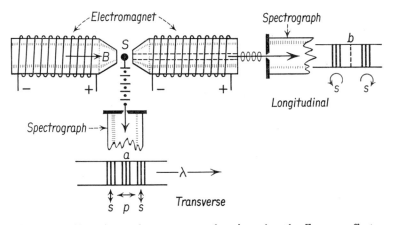

Figure 14 Experimental arrangement for observing the Zeeman effect.

emitted from S that appears as a single spectrum line at a and b when the magnetic field is off would appear as shown in the diagram when the field is turned on. If the field is strengthened the line spacing and the over-all width of each pattern increase. If the field is weakened the lines come closer together.

When the light of the different lines in each Zeeman pattern is tested for polarization, the transverse components are found to be plane polarized as may be seen from the double-ended arrows in the diagram. The letters p and s refer to the transverse components as they are polarized parallel and perpendicularly, respectively, to the field direction B. Only the s-components appear in the longitudinal light pattern and these are circularly polarized as may be judged by the circular arrows in the diagram.

INTERPRETATION OF THE ZEEMAN EFFECT

The fact that each spectrum line spreads into a pattern of lines when the light source is located in a magnetic field has been interpreted to mean that the energy levels of the initial and final states of the atom are split into a number of levels. To understand the reason for this, consider an atom with its electron in a $^2P_{3/2}$ state (Figure 13). In this state the orbital and spin momenta are oriented as shown in the second diagram from the left in Figure 7. Both are precessing rapidly around their resultant j^* (Figure 12).

When the atom finds its electron in a ^2P state with $j=3/2$, the quantum conditions of atomic structure require that j^* take only specified directions with respect to the magnetic induction B. In this case, there are *only four* possible orientations (Figure 15). The angle that j^* makes with the B direction is found in the following way: the angular momentum

$$j^* = \sqrt{j(j+1)}\,\frac{h}{2\pi}$$

projected on B must have values of

$$p = m\frac{h}{2\pi}$$

with m the *magnetic quantum number* given by

$$m = \pm 1/2,\ \pm 3/2,\ \pm 5/2 \ldots,\ \pm j.$$

In our example of $j = 3/2$ ($j^* = 1.94\ h/2\pi$) and $m = +3/2$, $+1/2$, $-1/2$, and $-3/2$, each of the m values corresponds to a different energy level. Thus, when the magnetic field is turned on, this $^2P_{3/2}$ level splits into four equally spaced levels designated by these four different magnetic quantum numbers.

The general result of the magnetic field is to split all levels into $2j+1$ magnetic levels. Furthermore, transitions between two field-free levels normally producing a single spectrum line will now give rise to a number of lines. Transitions obeying the selection rule $\triangle m = +1, 0,$ or -1 then yield symmetrical pattern lines.

A schematic diagram of an atom with its valence electron in

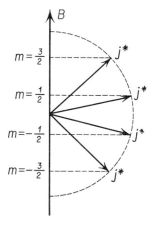

Figure 15 Space quantization of an atom in a magnetic field showing the allowed orientations for $j = 3/2$.

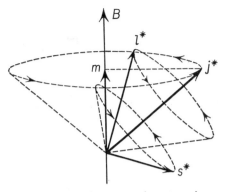

Figure 16 Schematic diagram of a precessing atom in a magnetic field B.

a $j = 3/2$ and $m = +3/2$ state may be seen in Figure 16. While the spin and orbit precess speedily around their resultant j^*, j^* precesses more slowly around the field direction B. The latter precessional frequency increases proportionately with the field. When B falls to zero, only the precession of j^* drops to zero.

6 THE VECTOR MODEL, NUCLEAR SPIN, AND MOLECULES

One of the best proofs of the existence of discrete, or distinct, energy states within the atom may be found in the experiments performed in 1914 by Franck and Hertz. For two decades following these investigations, other physicists refined the original techniques and extended the observations to many different elements. Franck and Hertz bombarded a vapor, sodium, with electrons from a heated tungsten filament. This is what happened.

Electrons from the hot filament F (Figure 1) were accelerated toward a grid G by a positive charge obtained from a battery B. A weak but opposing electric field was applied between the plate P and the grid. The vapor pressure in the tube during the experiments was such as to make the *mean-free-path* of the particles about half the distance from F to G.

In the experiments, if an electron starts from rest at F and

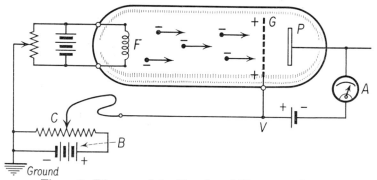

Figure 1   Diagram of the Franck and Hertz experiment.

reaches G without an encounter of any kind it will probably pass through to the plate and be registered as part of a current shown by the milliammeter. As the contact C moves slowly but continuously to the right, the grid voltage V increases continuously; the electron acquires higher and higher velocities before reaching P and G. But as the current in the plate rises, it soon reaches a maximum and then decreases to a minimum; then rises to a maximum again, then decreases to minimum, etc.

The rise and fall of the current may be explained in this way: When the electrons from F achieve a high enough speed they may encounter an atom, and in collision with it may impart enough energy to raise the valence electron from its normal state to the first excited state. In so doing, the bombarding electron loses most of its energy and lacks the amount needed to reach P. At higher voltages, the electrons making collisions and losing energy will nevertheless retain enough to carry them on to the plate, causing the current to rise again. At still higher voltages, each electron will have sufficient energy to engage in two collisions, one after the other, and thus excite two different atoms. Or these collisions may lift the electron to a higher energy level and in some instances even remove the valence electron from the atom entirely. This latter process is *ionization*.

The basic equation expressing the electron velocity v and its kinetic energy $\frac{1}{2}mv^2$ in terms of the applied voltage V is

$$Ve = \tfrac{1}{2}mv^2.$$

By observing the voltages at which peak currents are reached in the Franck-Hertz experiments, we can determine the minimum voltage required to raise the valence electron from its normal state to the lowest excited state, or to remove it from the atom altogether. These minimum voltages are known respectively as the *excitation* and *ionization* potentials.

The excitation potential of sodium atoms is 2.10 volts, whereas the ionization potential is 5.09 volts. The first of these values agrees exactly with the energy hv of the yellow line in the visible spectrum of sodium. The second value agrees with hv_∞, where v_∞ represents the frequency of the limit of the principal series of spectrum lines. From an energy standpoint

$$Ve = hv.$$

This basic equation is part of the general law of conservation of energy and is, therefore, of great importance in accounting for many atomic processes.

Figure 2 is a graph of the ionization potentials of elements throughout the periodic table. The higher the ionization potential of an element, the stronger is the binding energy that holds it in the atom. Note the low binding energies of the alkali metals where the new outer subshells begin to be filled. The strongest binding energies are those for the inert gases in which the subshells are completely filled.

VECTOR MODEL FOR TWO ELECTRONS

In the discussion of the external structure of atoms we have been concerned to this point with atoms containing only one valence electron. These are the atoms of hydrogen and the alkali metals. There are a number of elements in the periodic table, however, which have two valence electrons. The question arises, therefore, as to how these account for the observed spectrum lines.

Consider the alkaline earth elements in which each atom contains two electrons in an outermost electron subshell. In the normal state all electrons are in completed subshells. These may be indicated as follows:

$$1s^2 \ \underset{\text{Be}}{2s^2} \ 2p^6 \ \underset{\text{Mg}}{3s^2} \ 3p^6 \ \underset{\text{Ca}}{4s^2} \ 3d^{10} \ 4p^6 \ \underset{\text{Sr}}{5s^2} \ 4d^{10} \ 5p^6 \ \underset{\text{Ba}}{6s^2} \ 4f^{14} \ 5d^{10} \ 6p^6 \ \underset{\text{Ra}}{7s^2}$$

$$Z = 4 \qquad\quad 12 \qquad 20 \qquad\qquad 38 \qquad\qquad\quad 56 \qquad\qquad\qquad\qquad 88$$

Each neutral atom with its atomic number is shown directly

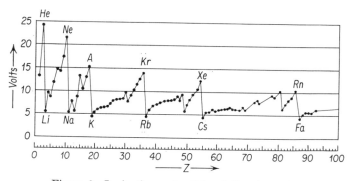

Figure 2   Ionization potentials of the elements.

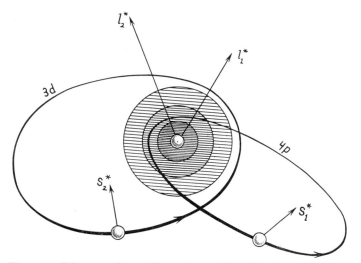

Figure 3   Diagram of a calcium atom with both valence electrons excited to outer orbits.

below its last and outermost filled subshell. These are underlined and are the valence electrons in s-orbits.

When one of these elements is vaporized in an electrical discharge tube, the emitted light from each atom results from the excitation of one or both of its valence electrons. If only one electron is excited into an outer orbit, both are then in incompleted subshells. When this electron jumps back to an allowable orbit, light is emitted.

If, as the result of an atomic collision in the discharge tube, both valence electrons become excited to outer orbits, both will jump back simultaneously and the atom will emit one light quantum only. Since both electrons may be excited and involved in the radiation of light, it is not surprising to find greater numbers of energy levels, as well as spectrum lines, in elements like calcium than there are for one-valence electron atoms like sodium.

With two electrons taking part in the formation of different atomic states, four angular momenta are involved in quantization. These result from the two orbits with angular momenta l^*_1 and l^*_2 and the two electron spins s^*_1 and s^*_2 (Figure 3). In many atoms the two spins are strongly coupled together to form a resultant spin angular momentum S^*, and the orbital angular momenta are coupled together to form a resultant L^*. The two

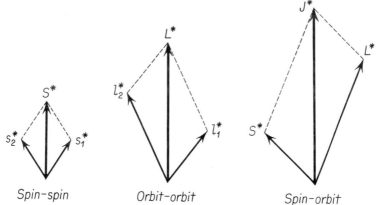

Figure 4   Vector model for two electrons illustrating LS (Russell-Saunders) coupling.

resultants S^* and L^* are more loosely coupled together to form a final resultant J^* (Figure 4).

Consider for purposes of illustration two electrons in orbits $4p$ and $3d$ respectively. Their spin and orbital quantum numbers are $s = 1/2$ and $l = 1$ for the $4p$-electron, and $s = 1/2$ and $l = 2$ for the $3d$-electron. When the angular momenta for these quantum numbers are combined properly the allowable values of the spin and orbital resultants provide that S^* equals zero or 1 and L^* equals 1, 2, or 3. These values may be obtained simply by adding both spin and orbital quantum numbers, by subtracting them, and by including all whole numbers between.

When the angular momenta of these spins and orbitals are combined in pairs, each of the J-values resulting from the combination corresponds to an actual observable energy level. Altogether there are twelve possible energy levels in which these two electrons $4p$ and $3d$ may exist in the atom. Levels with a spin $S = 0$ are called *singlet* levels; those with $S = 1$ are called *triplet* levels. It is common practice to designate the L-values for all atomic energy states with capital letters as follows:

$$L = 0 \quad 1 \quad 2 \quad 3 \quad 4 \quad 5 \dots$$
$$ S \quad P \quad D \quad F \quad G \quad H \dots$$

Hence we may represent the twelve allowable energy levels for the electron configuration $4p\ 3d$ as:

$$^1P_1 \quad {}^1D_2 \quad {}^1F_3 \quad {}^3P_0 \quad {}^3P_1 \quad {}^3P_2 \quad {}^3D_1 \quad {}^3D_2 \quad {}^3D_3 \quad {}^3F_2 \quad {}^3F_3 \quad {}^3F_4.$$

If the two electrons of any specific atom are in any of these twelve levels and they jump simultaneously to some other pair of orbits with a multiplicity of allowable levels, many radiated frequencies may be observed. This accounts for the complexity of the many lined spectra known for all the alkaline earth elements.

When only one valence electron is excited in atoms with two valence electrons, the various permissible transitions back to the normal state give rise to a number of series of spectrum lines. Several of these series are observed in which each component is composed of three lines while several other series are composed of single lines. These arrays are called triplet series and singlet series, respectively.

THE PAULI EXCLUSION PRINCIPLE

We have already seen how the various quantum states of the electrons which compose the structure of the atom are expressed by quantum numbers. These numbers, four in all, are designated

$$n = \text{principle quantum number}$$
$$l = \text{orbital quantum number}$$
$$j = \text{inner quantum number}$$
$$m = \text{magnetic quantum number.}$$

No two or more electrons in the same atom can have all four quantum numbers alike. This is *the Pauli exclusion principle.* Thus, if two electrons have three quantum numbers alike, the fourth must be different. Suppose an electron is in an orbit in which $n = 3$ and $l = 1$. This orbit is designated $3p$. In the absence of a magnetic field there are two possible energy states for it to occupy. One of these is $3^2P_{1/2}$; for it $j = 1/2$. The other is $3^2P_{3/2}$ in which $j = 3/2$.

When the atom is in a magnetic field each of these levels splits into a number of other energy levels. The first one splits into two with magnetic quantum numbers $m = +1/2$ and $m = -1/2$, and the second into four with magnetic quantum numbers $m = +3/2$, $m = +1/2$, $m = -1/2$, and $m = -3/2$. From this, it becomes evident that there are six possible combinations. Thus, if there are to be several electrons in $3p$ orbits of the same atom, there are six possible energy states in which they can coexist, two of them with j equalling $1/2$ and four with j equalling $3/2$. A $3p$ subshell of electrons in any one atom, therefore, cannot contain more than six electrons; if it does contain six, no two of them may have the same m- and j-values.

Applied to other electron subshells, the Pauli principle shows there are only two allowable states for $l = 0$. These are $j = 1/2$ with $m = +1/2$ or $m = -1/2$. For a d-electron subshell, there are ten allowable states.

The Pauli exclusion principle is therefore in accord with the Bohr-Stoner Scheme (page 57) for the building up of the elements in the periodic table. It is considered the basic principle governing the number of elements in each period.

NUCLEAR SPIN AND HYPERFINE STRUCTURE

The first evidence that the nuclei of many atoms are endowed with a spin angular momentum similar to the electron's was presented by Pauli in 1924. Pauli's proposal has since become the means for explaining the *hyperfine structure of spectrum lines*.

Some of the spectral lines of certain elements are composed of a number of closely spaced lines. For some of these, this hyperfine structure forms similar and regular line patterns; for others, the patterns differ considerably and are quite complex. To account for this hyperfine structure we assign a spin angular momentum I^* to the nucleus. The formula is

$$I^* = \sqrt{I(I+1)}\,\frac{h}{2\pi}$$

in which $I = 1/2, 1, 3/2, 2, 5/2, 3 \cdots$ (Figure 5).

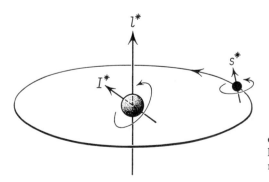

Figure 5 Both the electron and the nucleus have a spin angular momentum.

Any individual isotope has only one nuclear spin value. *The nuclear spin quantum number I is a half-integer when the atomic mass number is odd, and an integer when the atomic mass number is even.* A few examples illustrate the rule.

Nuclear Moments

Z	Atom	A	I	μ_I
1	$_1\text{H}^1$	1	1/2	+2.792
1	$_1\text{H}^2$	2	1	+0.857
2	$_2\text{He}^4$	4	0	0
3	$_3\text{Li}^6$	6	1	+0.822
3	$_3\text{Li}^7$	7	3/2	+3.256
8	$_8\text{O}^{17}$	17	5/2	−1.893
11	$_{11}\text{Na}^{23}$	23	3/2	+2.217
19	$_{19}\text{K}^{40}$	40	4	−1.291
27	$_{27}\text{Co}^{59}$	59	7/2	+4.648
49	$_{49}\text{In}^{113}$	113	9/2	+5.486
81	$_{81}\text{Tl}^{203}$	203	1/2	+1.611
83	$_{83}\text{Bi}^{209}$	209	9/2	+4.080

Because nuclei contain charged particles any spin angular momentum that might exist could be expected to produce a nuclear magnetic moment. In most cases this moment is positive, signifying that it is the result of a positive charge. But there are a substantial number of nuclei with a negative magnetic moment caused by a negative charge. The preceding table contains both negative and positive values for these moments in its final column.

Nuclear magnetic moments are measured in units called *nuclear magnetons.* One nuclear magneton equals 5.0493×10^{-24} erg/gauss. This is smaller than the Bohr magneton used to specify electron magnetic moments by the ratio of the proton mass to the electron mass, $1840/1$.

The common explanation for the negative nuclear moments is that the nucleons are complex particles. The neutron, for example, may be considered to consist of a proton plus an electron. Moreover, a neutron is known to have an angular momentum of $1/2$ and a magnetic moment of -1.913 nuclear magnetons.

The effect of a nuclear spin on the atomic energy levels is to split each of them into several very close component levels. The jumping of an electron from one level to another that otherwise would have given rise to a single spectrum line will now produce a number of closely spaced lines.

In each of these hyperfine energy levels, the atom is visualized in a way that couples the resultant angular momentum J^* of the external electrons with the nuclear angular momentum I^*. The combination of J^* and I^* yields the resultant angular momentum of the atom F^*, written as

$$F^* = \sqrt{F(F+1)}\,\frac{h}{2\pi}\cdot$$

F is the *hyperfine structure quantum number*.

MOLECULAR SPECTRA

When an electrical discharge is sent through a rarefied gas, we may observe frequently a band spectrum of molecules in addition to the line spectrum of free atoms. The general subject is exceedingly complex. We shall narrow our examination to the diatomic molecules, those of two atoms.

Figure 6 contains five bands of a typical band spectrum. The dark edge of each band is called the *band head* and the fading end is called the *band tail*. Molecules of carbon monoxide, iodine, and sulfur each show one band progression, while those of phosphorus nitrate show several. A large part of our knowledge of the structure of diatomic molecules has been gained from the band spectra of such molecules as

$$\begin{array}{lllll} H_2 & C_2 & CN & HI & CaH \\ O_2 & P_2 & PN & HF & AlH \\ N_2 & S_2 & NO & HCl & AgCl \end{array}$$

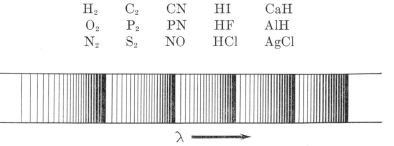

$\lambda \longrightarrow$

Figure 6   Diagram of a typical progression of bands in the spectrum of a diatomic molecule.

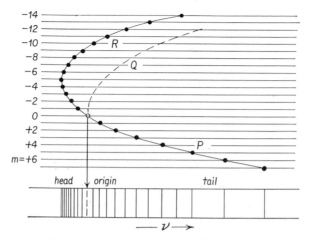

Figure 7   A Fortrat diagram and details of a single band as seen in the spectrum of cyanogen (CN molecule).

When each band is photographed under high dispersion and resolving power, it is found to be composed of many fine lines. As in atomic spectra these lines are images of the slit of the spectrograph and correspond to the different wavelengths of light emitted by the molecule. Figure 7 is a diagram of a single band in which the individual lines are shown plotted graphically and also as they appear in the photographed spectrum. The missing line at $m = 0$ is the *band origin* and the arms of the parabola are called the P-branch and R-branch respectively. A graph of this kind is called a Fortrat diagram.

Some bands contain a third branch of lines, the Q-branch, also shown in Figure 7.

MOLECULAR ROTATION

Three kinds of quantized motions within the structure of the molecule account for the band spectra of diatomic molecules. These are rotation, vibration, and electronic.

Figure 8 illustrates the rotational motion of a molecule. Like a double star in the firmament, the two atoms rotate around their common center of mass C. The mechanical, or kinetic, energy of this rotating system is written as $\mathcal{E} = \frac{1}{2}I\omega^2$ with ω representing the angular velocity and I the moment of inertia.

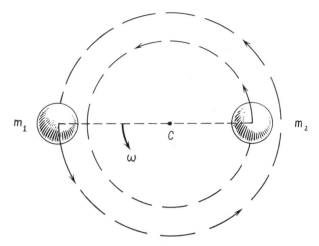

Figure 8   A diatomic molecule rotates around its center of mass.

Like the electron structure of the atom, it is the angular momentum and not the energy that is quantized. The quantum conditions governing this kind of rotator are expressed as

$$J^* = \sqrt{J(J+1)}\ h/2\pi.$$

In this equation, J^* designates the angular momentum $I\omega$ and J is the rotational quantum number which can only be a whole number.

$$J = 0, 1, 2, 3, 4, 5, 6, \cdot\ \cdot\ \cdot.$$

Each value of J corresponds to a different angular momentum and to a distinct energy level. When a molecule rotates with one particular angular momentum, it is in an excited quantum state. If the angular momentum suddenly decreases the difference in energy released is a light wave of energy $h\nu$. The transitions between the rotational energy levels of a molecule are restricted to changes of one unit only, that is, plus or minus 1, and the radiated frequencies lie in the long wavelength part of the infrared spectrum.

MOLECULAR VIBRATION

As the two atoms of a diatomic molecule rotate around their common center of mass, they also vibrate back and forth along a straight line drawn through their respective centers of mass

(Figure 9). This vibratory motion is subject to the quantum conditions expresed by

$$\mathscr{E}_{\mathrm{vib}} = (v + 1/2)B$$

in which v is the *vibrational quantum number,* an integer, and B is a constant whose value changes from one molecule to another.

When a molecule is in its normal state the vibrational quantnum number v equals zero and the rotational quantum number J also equals zero. In collision with another atomic particle, the normal molecule acquires additional energy; then the vibrational energy may increase to a value of 1, 2, or 3, etc., and the rotational energy may increase similarly.

From an excited state, the molecule may return to its normal state by a series of transitions in which vibration and rotation change independently; or they may both change simultaneously with the emission of a single light quantum $h\nu$. Thus there are many ways for the molecule to return to its normal state and many different frequencies that it can radiate.

ELECTRON TRANSITIONS

Figure 10 contains a schematic diagram of a carbon monoxide molecule. A carbon nucleus of charge 6 and an oxygen nucleus of

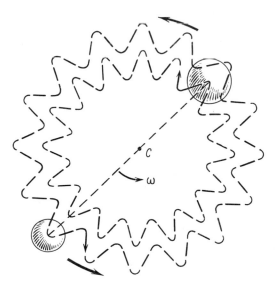

Figure 9 A diatomic molecule vibrates along a line through the two atomic centers at the same time that it rotates about its center of mass.

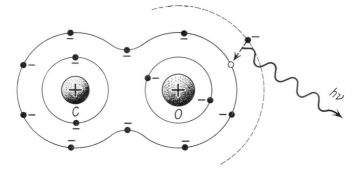

Figure 10 Schematic diagram of a CO molecule undergoing an electronic transition.

charge 8 are bound together by a total of fourteen electrons to become a neutral molecule. Suppose that by some collision process one of the outermost electrons becomes excited to an outer quantized orbit. In returning to the normal state, a photon of light is emitted. This light will be in or near the visible spectrum.

If there are also changes in rotational and vibrational energy during the electronic transition, a multiplicity of different frequencies will be radiated. When, for example, an electron transition is accompanied by a simultaneous change from $v = 2$ to $v = 1$ and a rotational change from $J = 3$ to $J = 2$, a single frequency is emitted.

Now the different spectrum lines of a single band (Figure 7) result from the rotational changes accompanied by the same vibrational and electronic transitions. The different bands of a sequence (Figure 6), on the other hand, result from different vibrational changes accompanied by the same electronic transitions. The over-all concept then demonstrates that any specific electron transition occurring within a molecule determines the major change in molecular energy and therefore the general region of the spectrum—ultraviolet, visible, or infrared—in which a band sequence will occur. The vibrational changes determine the relative positions of the band origins, and the rotational changes govern the structure of the band.

7 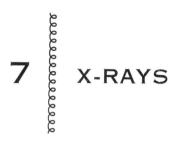 X-RAYS

DISCOVERY OF X-RAYS

Ever since their discovery in 1895 by a German Nobel prize winner, Wilhelm Roentgen, x-rays have been of immense value in the investigations of atomic physics and have added incalculably to our knowledge of the structure of the atom. Roentgen's discovery came about from the physicist's studies of electric discharges through gases. While operating a discharge tube in an experiment, he observed a fluorescence on a distant screen which he reasoned was caused by radiations that could penetrate opaque materials. These radiations he called *x-rays*.

The uses of the rays discovered by Roentgen were not limited

Figure 1   Wilhelm Konrad Roentgen (1845–1923). Discoverer of x-rays. (*Courtesy of General Electric X-ray Department.*)

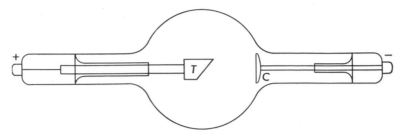

Figure 2   A gas-discharge x-ray tube. *C* is the cathode and *T* is the target.

to the physics laboratory. Almost immediately after discovery, they were adapted by physicians as aids in medical diagnosis and eventually in therapy. Industry turned to them, too, for the study of properties and internal structure of materials, and for examination of castings to check for flaws. The newly found x-rays, in other words, had a ready acceptance as tools for applied as well as basic science.

PRODUCTION OF X-RAYS

X-rays are produced whenever a stream of electrons strikes some substance. Three types of tubes in general use produce them. An early type (Figure 2) utilizes the electrons set free in a low-pressure gas-discharge tube by the bombardment of the cathode

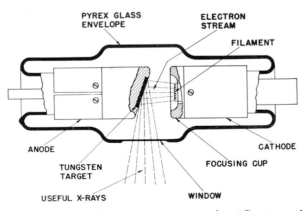

Figure 3   A modern Coolidge type x-ray tube. (*Courtesy of General Electric X-ray Department.*)

C by positive ions driven by the difference in potential between the target T and the cathode. The liberated electrons, also referred to as cathode rays, can be focused on any desired region by curving the cathode properly, since it will be remembered that cathode rays leave a cathode by moving perpendicular to its surface. If the difference of potential between T and C is indicated by V, the electrons reach the target with an amount of energy represented by Ve, e again the charge of the electron. The target in this type of tube thus becomes a source of x-rays. These tubes usually operate at about 30,000 to 50,000 volts.

In the second type of tube (Figure 3), the source of electrons is a heated filament with the vacuum in the tube made as complete as possible. The filament may be heated by a battery or a step-down transformer. The filament is generally surrounded by a metallic cup shaped to achieve the proper focusing of the electron beam. One of the principal advantages of this type of tube is the greater ease in controlling its current and voltage. A high voltage applied to the terminals of the tube accelerates the electrons to the target which then becomes the source of x-rays. Such tubes, sometimes called Coolidge x-ray tubes, have been operated at voltages ranging from a few hundred to approximately a million. The higher the voltage across the tube, the stronger the penetrating power of the x-rays it produces.

The third type of x-ray tube is a device called a *betatron* developed in 1941 by D. W. Kerst. It is coming into general use wherever x-rays of enormous penetrating power are required. A betatron consists of a doughnut-shaped vacuum tube placed between the poles of a large electromagnet (Figure 4). We can see how a betatron operates by examining a diagram of the cross-section of its doughnut-shaped tube (Figure 5). Electrons from a heated filament F are accelerated by a small difference in potential through a grid G. An alternating magnetic field is applied perpendicular to the path of the electrons. This produces two effects: the electron is forced to travel in a circular path of radius R at right angles to the magnetic field; and, since the field is changing, an induced electromotive force is produced which is tangent to the circular path and thus accelerates the electron. The electron picks up speed and extra kinetic energy as it circulates in the path. The pole pieces of the electromagnet

Figure 4 The 100,000,000 electron-volt betatron. The tube is in the center between the poles of the electromagnet. (*Courtesy of General Electric Company.*)

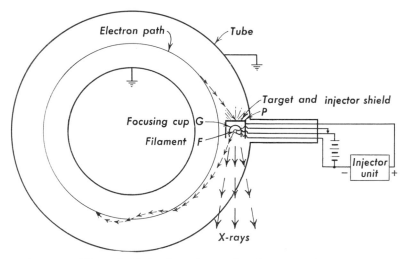

Figure 5 Path of an electron in a betatron tube.

have to be shaped with care so that the magnetic field at every instant will be of the right form in order to keep the electrons moving in the same circular orbit.

The alternating magnetic field is produced by supplying 60-cycle alternating current to the field coils of the electromagnet. The electrons are injected into the tube for a very short time at the beginning of a cycle of the alternating current, and then continue traveling around the circular orbit until the magnetic field reaches its maximum value in 1/240 sec. Each electron makes several hundred thousand revolutions in this quarter of a cycle. During each revolution the electron gains additional energy. When the electron acquires its maximum energy, current is sent through an auxiliary set of coils; this changes the magnetic field and the electron moves into a larger orbit and strikes the back of the plate P, which acts as the target, becoming the source of the x-rays.

Betatrons now operate at energies reaching 300 Mev. Modified forms of betatrons are being designed to operate at even higher energies. An unusual feature of the betatron as an x-ray tube is the fact that the x-rays come out in the forward direction instead of coming out in all directions from the target P. The x-rays are virtually confined within a small angle, from 2° to 15°, with respect to the forward direction. By suitable modification of the betatron, the high-energy electrons may be conducted out of the tube. Then they may be used for the study of atomic and nuclear phenomena.

SOME PROPERTIES OF X-RAYS

X-rays are invisible to the eye. But they can be detected by their blackening of a photographic plate or by the ionization they produce when passing through a gas or vapor. The intensity of the x-rays may be measured by the ionization they generate in a specially designed ionization chamber (Figure 6). The x-rays enter the chamber through a thin window of mica or aluminum and ionize the gas in the chamber. A difference of potential between the rod R and cylinder C causes these ions to move. The motion of the ions constitutes the current in the chamber. This current, though very small, can be measured with an electrometer E, or it may first be amplified with the aid of an amplifying

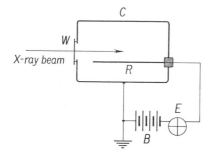

Figure 6 Ionization chamber and electrometer for measuring the intensity of x-rays.

circuit using radio tubes. The amplified current can then be measured with a galvanometer.

Besides being able to blacken a photographic plate and ionize gases, x-rays can penetrate various thicknesses of substances including ones that are opaque to visible radiation. In their passage through matter, some of the x-rays are absorbed; their energy is converted into other forms. But some of the x-rays pass through; these can be detected and measured. The amount of energy absorbed depends on the atomic number of the substance, upon its density and thickness, and the wavelength of the x-rays in question. If a beam of x-rays is sent through a composite substance made of different types of materials, the photograph can be used to reveal the nature of these materials and their locations within the substance (Figure 7).

ORIGIN AND NATURE OF X-RAYS

In each of the x-ray tubes we have described, x-rays are produced whenever electrons strike a target. From a microscopic or subatomic point of view, every target consists of atoms composed of positively charged nuclei surrounded by electrons. When an external electron enters a target it exerts forces on these charges. In some cases, it sets the charges into vibration, in other cases, it causes the separation of electrons from atoms— that is, it produces ions. In the process these electrons yield energy to the atomic particles. Some of this energy is converted into heat in the target, while some of it is radiated from the atoms in the form of electromagnetic waves.

During its motion through the target, the external electron itself is subjected to forces and is accelerated. The acceleration may take the form of a change of speed, a change in direction, or both. From electromagnetic theory, we know that an accelerated charge radiates energy in the form of electromagnetic waves. Consequently, the incident electron also loses energy by the radiation of electromagnetic waves.

The rate at which a charge radiates energy depends on the square of the charge—e^2—and the square of its acceleration—a^2—if the speed is small in comparison with the speed of light. We may, therefore, expect x-rays to be similar in nature to other electromagnetic waves such as light and radio waves, but probably much smaller in wavelength. Were this radiation to be analyzed, it could be resolved into two parts, one of them dependent upon the energy and motion of the electron involved and the other on the nature of the atoms in the target.

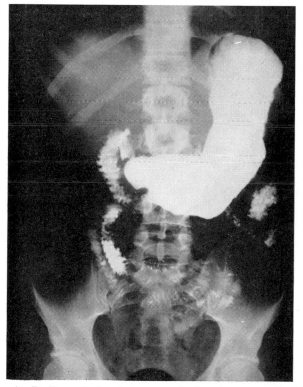

Figure 7   Radiograph showing opaque barium in a stomach. (*Courtesy of General Electric X-ray Department.*)

The existence of a wave motion may be proven only by the presence of interference and diffraction phenomena. In the earliest experiments on diffraction in 1899, x-rays were sent through a narrow slit between two pieces of lead and permitted to fall on a photographic plate. Some diffraction pattern appeared on the plate, but available instruments at the time lacked sufficient resolving power to show the bright and dark lines of the pattern. The best that could be said then was that if x-rays were waves, their wavelengths were quite short, approximately 10^{-8} or 10^{-9} cm.

In diffraction experiments with visible light, the distance between lines on a diffraction grating approximates the wavelength of light. Now the distance between atoms and molecules in crystals is known to be about 10^{-8} cm. It is known also that these atoms and molecules are arranged in regular patterns.

In 1912, it occurred to M. von Laue that crystals fulfilled all the conditions for diffraction of x-rays. This suggested that ordinary crystals might be used as diffraction gratings. In an experiment conducted with his co-workers, Laue sent a narrow pencil of x-rays through a crystal onto a photographic plate. There he observed a definite diffraction pattern. This was the first conclusive demonstration that x-rays were waves.

DIFFRACTION AND INTERFERENCE OF X-RAYS

From the experiments of Laue and his collaborators, x-rays are shown to have the same nature as light and radio waves, electromagnetic but of very short wavelength. When a pencil of rays is sent through a small, thin crystal, such as a piece of rock salt (Figure 8), the photograph on the plate which the x-rays strike will show a series of small spots arranged in a fixed pattern. This pattern (Figure 9) is a diffraction pattern. It is formed

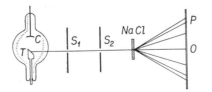

Figure 8 Arrangement of apparatus for producing a Laue diffraction pattern using a rock salt (NaCl) crystal. S_1 and S_2 are pinholes and P is the photographic plate.

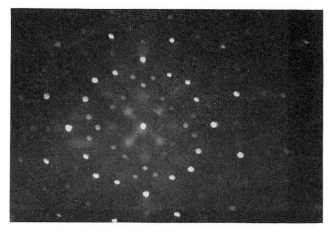

Figure 9   Photograph of Laue diffraction pattern of rock salt. (*From photograph by J. G. Dash.*)

by the action of the ions of the crystal because of their regular arrangement in the crystal. The crystal now acts as a three-dimensional grating and the pattern resulting on the photographic plate is called a Laue pattern. From the distribution and intensities of the points on the plate, the arrangement of the ions in the crystal can be deduced.

A somewhat different arrangement of the x-ray beam and crystal used by W. H. Bragg provides a simpler, more readily interpreted pattern. In this scheme (Figure 10), x-rays coming from the target T of the x-ray tube pass through two narrow slits and then strike the face of the crystal which is mounted on a spectrometer table. The crystal scatters the x-rays in all directions, but the photographic plate is so set that it receives only those rays that come from the face of the crystal. The angle θ between the original beam and the face of the crystal is changed slowly by rotating the crystal.

In general, the photograph will show a series of sharp lines against a continuous background. An ionization chamber may be substituted for the photographic plate. In this case, the chamber measures the intensity of the x-ray beam entering it. With a narrow slit in front of the chamber's window, the intensity of the x-ray beam coming from the crystal is at maximum when the

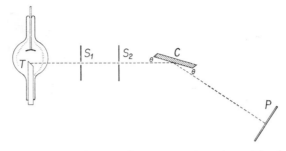

Figure 10 The single crystal x-ray spectrometer with photographic plate. S_1 and S_2 are narrow slits, C is the crystal and P is the photographic plate.

beam forms an angle θ with the face of the crystal. For this reason the beam is said sometimes to be "reflected" from the crystal.

CRYSTAL AS A DIFFRACTION GRATING

To understand how a crystal functions as a diffraction grating for x-rays, consider the simplest type of crystal, the cubic crystal, such as rock salt (NaCl). Its cubic structure (Figure 11) is known from crystallographic studies. The crystal consists of sodium ions (Na+) and chlorine ions (Cl-) located at the corners of a cube. Each sodium ion is surrounded by six chlorine ions and each chlorine ion is surrounded by six sodium ions. The distance d between the centers of two adjacent ions can be obtained from a knowledge of the molecular weight of salt, its density and the value of the Avogadro number. At the present time the accepted value is

$$d = 2.82 \times 10^{-8} \text{ cm.}$$

When x-rays pass through a crystal the electric field of their waves sets the electric charges of the sodium and chlorine into vibration with the same frequency as the waves themselves. The ions act as new sources of waves, sending them out in all directions. To find the effect of these waves at any point outside the crystal we must determine the phases—or synchronization— of the waves from all the ions that reach this point. The phase relations, in general, are such that the waves annul each other

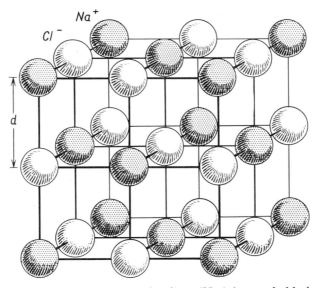

Figure 11 The arrangement of sodium (Na⁺) ions and chlorine (Cl⁻) ions in a crystal of salt.

except at a few points where they meet in the same phase. The diffraction pattern then consists of a fixed number of intense spots in an arrangement determined by the spacings of the ions as diffraction centers. One easy way for finding the positions of the intense spots was developed by W. L. Bragg:

Suppose that a set of parallel planes passes through the centers of atoms or ions spaced a distance d apart. These planes are drawn as parallel lines (Figure 12). Then suppose that x-rays of wavelength λ enter the crystal at angle θ to the planes. Al-

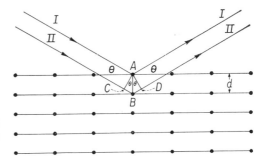

Figure 12 Reflection of x-rays from atomic planes.

though the waves are now scattered in all directions, let us look only at those rays deflected at an angle θ similar to mirror reflection.

For simplicity, consider just two rays I and II which are scattered from atoms A and B respectively. Ray II obviously travels a longer distance through the crystal than ray I. Had they started in phase, they would differ in phase by the distance $CB + BD$ on leaving the crystal. These waves reinforce each other only if this difference in path is a whole number of wavelengths, $n \lambda$, with n representing an integer. Stated in terms of the distance d between the atomic planes and the angle θ, this condition for constructive interference is expressed by the equation

$$n \lambda = 2d \sin \theta.$$

This is known as the *Bragg equation*. If d, sometimes called the *grating space* of the crystal, is known, the wavelength of the x-rays producing the intense maxima may be calculated. On the other hand, we can find the distance between the atomic planes of the crystal by using x-rays of known wavelengths.

The Bragg equation has other applications. It is not limited to atomic planes parallel to the surface of the crystal. Sets of parallel planes can be constructed at different angles throughout a crystal (Figure 13). The value of the grating space d is dif-

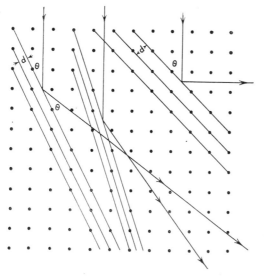

Figure 13 Reflection of x-rays from sets of atomic planes within a crystal to produce the Laue diffraction pattern.

ferent for the various sets of planes. These values of d are
related by simple geometric conditions. The x-rays scattered
from any set of parallel planes will reinforce each other only if
a specific wavelength is present to satisfy the Bragg qualifica-
tion. Moreover, there will be an appreciable intense spot only if
there are enough atoms in the plane. The Bragg equation, therefore, may also serve to determine the positions of the intense
spots in a Laue diffraction pattern.

8 X-RAY SPECTRA AND ATOMIC STRUCTURE

Analysis of the x-rays emanating from an element used as a target in an x-ray tube yields valuable information on the structure of the atom and on some of the properties of the radiation. Figure 1 shows the spectrum of the x-rays from a molybdenum target when the tube is operated at 35,000 volts.

These rays were analyzed with a single crystal spectrometer using an ionization chamber as the detector. The intensity of the x-rays was plotted on a graph against the wavelength of the

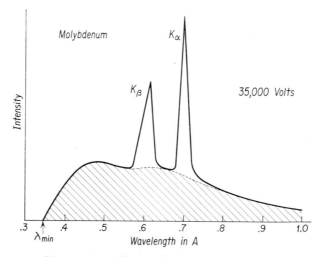

Figure 1 Characteristic K_α and K_β lines superposed on the continuous x-ray spectrum of molybdenum.

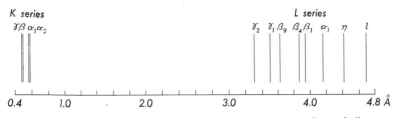

Figure 2   Relative positions of the K and L series x-ray lines of silver.

x-rays, found through the aid of the Bragg equation. The graph (Figure 1) shows some important things: first, there is a *continuous* x-ray spectrum shown by shading that starts at some fixed minimum wavelength, λ_{min}, then increases in intensity as the wavelength grows and then drops off slowly; second, two sharp lines, K_α and K_β, which are part of the sharp line spectrum characteristic of the element, are superimposed on the continuous spectrum.

The curve does not go beyond one angstrom unit—10^{-8} or one hundred-millionth of a centimeter—because the x-rays of longer wavelength are almost completely absorbed by the glass of the x-ray tube and the air through which they pass on the way to the ionization chamber. The examination of longer wavelengths requires use of x-ray tubes with very thin windows and spectrographs operated in a vacuum. In these circumstances, many more sharp lines are seen. Figure 2 shows the positions of the sharp line x-ray spectrum of silver from approximately 0.4A to 4.8A. Instruments of high resolving power disclose some of the lines, such as K_α, as doublets; that is, two lines very close together. The $K_{\alpha 1}$ and $K_{\alpha 2}$ lines of silver, for example, have wavelengths of 0.558A and 0.563A respectively.

THE CONTINUOUS X-RAY SPECTRUM

The source of the continuous x-ray spectrum can be traced to the radiation produced by the acceleration of electrons as they strike the target of the x-ray tube. In the process of acceleration, the electrons pass through the electric field of force of the nuclei of the target atoms. The intensity of the x-rays is governed by the power supplied to the tube and the atomic number of the element used as the target.

One other interesting aspect of the continuous spectrum is the existence of a short wavelength limit (Figure 1). Experiments show this short wavelength limit to be independent of the target element. If the voltage across the x-ray tube is varied, the value of the short wavelength limit decreases with the increase of voltage. Since the frequency of radiation varies inversely with the wavelength, the maximum frequency, ν_{max}, of the continuous spectrum is directly proportionate to the voltage across the tube.

A simpler explanation may be given on the basis of an inverse photoelectric effect. Put this way, the maximum energy an electron can give out when stopped by a target is emitted in the form of a single photon of energy $h\nu_{max}$. Since the maximum energy of an electron in an x-ray tube is the voltage multiplied by the electronic charge Ve, we may express this fact by the equation

$$Ve = h\nu_{max}.$$

The measurement of the short wavelength limit of the continuous x-ray spectrum and the voltage to obtain it provides a means for determining h/e. By knowing the electronic charge e, we can find the Planck constant h.

THE SHARP LINE X-RAY SPECTRUM

The first systematic study of sharp line spectra of the elements was made by H. G. J. Moseley in 1913. He used a vacuum type Bragg spectrometer. Each element investigated was made the target of an x-ray tube. He found that all these elements produced similar types of spectra. Moseley classified the x-ray spectral lines from each element into two groups or series: one of comparatively short wavelengths, the K series, and the other of comparatively long wavelengths, the L series. The two are widely separated from one another in wavelength (Figure 2). Some of the heavier elements with atomic numbers above 66 also have other x-ray spectral series, designated as M and N series, with even longer wavelengths than the L series.

Moseley sought some simple relationship between characteristic spectra and the properties of atoms. He found one and presented it in the form of a graph (Figure 3). In it, he plotted the square root of the frequency of a characteristic line, in this case the K_α line, against the atomic number of the element

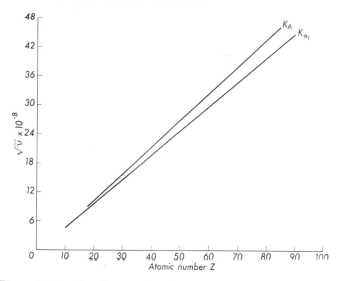

Figure 3 Moseley diagram in which the square root of the frequency is plotted against the atomic number of the emitting element for two lines of the *K* series.

emitting the line. The graphic result was a straight line. Each graph of this kind has come to be known as a *Moseley diagram.*

The significance of Moseley's work becomes apparent if we recall that in 1913 the atomic number of an element reflected its place among the elements according to atomic weight. To obtain a straight line for his diagram Moseley had to rearrange the orders of nickel and cobalt, assigning a lower atomic number to the element of higher atomic weight. Moreover, he had to leave a gap at $Z = 43$ to show that an element of this atomic number was missing. This element has since been found; it is called *technetium.*

The Moseley diagram can be used—and it has been—to find the atomic number of an element when its characteristic x-ray spectrum has been determined. The equation of any line on the Moseley diagram can be expressed as

$$\nu^{\frac{1}{2}} = C_1 \left(Z - a_1 \right),$$

with C_1 symbolizing the slope of the line and a_1 the point of intercept. These values can be determined from the graph.

ORIGIN OF THE CHARACTERISTIC X-RAYS

The high frequencies and short wavelengths of the x-ray lines along with the high voltages needed to produce them suggests that an atom undergoes large energy changes when releasing x-rays. These energy changes involve those electrons close to the nucleus. Many different experiments lead to the conclusion that the electrons of an atom are grouped in certain shells or levels. These levels are designated by either a letter, or a number (page 59). The letters begin with K for the innermost levels and continue with L, M, etc., for the outer levels. The numbers are called the *principal quantum numbers* and are obtained from the extension of Niels Bohr's theory of the hydrogen spectrum to the x-ray spectra of the elements.

The K level is assigned the principal quantum number 1, the L level gets the number 2, etc. All the heavier elements have a K level of principal quantum number 1, containing two electrons. These elements also have an L level, of principal quantum number 2, containing eight electrons in the normal state. Some atoms also have M, N, etc., levels of principal quantum numbers 3, 4, etc. respectively.

The fact that all heavier elements emit lines of the K series indicates that these series have common origins. This holds similarly true for elements emitting L series lines and M series lines. The frequency, for example, of the K_α line, the most intense of the K series, may be written in the algebraic form

$$\nu = cR(Z-1)^2 (1/1^2 - 1/2^2).$$

In this equation R is the *Rydberg constant,* c the velocity of light and Z the atomic number of the element emitting the line of frequency ν. The interpretation of this equation is that the line is given off when an electron moves from the orbit of principal quantum number 2 to the orbit of principal quantum number 1.

To understand why the factor $(Z-1)$ appears in the equation rather than Z, consider how x-rays are produced. In the atoms of elements studied, the orbits of principal quantum numbers 1 and 2 are completely filled (Figure 4). An electron from the cathode of the x-ray tube approaches the target with an amount of energy Ve, V being the voltage of the tube. When the electron approaches an atom in the target, the electron may, if

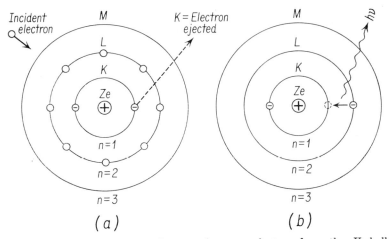

Figure 4 (*a*) Incident electron ejects an electron from the *K*-shell. (*b*) Electron from *L*-shell goes to *K*-shell and atom emits a photon of energy *h*ν.

it has enough energy, knock out an electron from the orbit for which $n = 1$.

Since the other electrons in the atom remain in their normal states, the electron that gets knocked out of the innermost orbit has to leave the atom. In other words, the atom becomes ionized by the removal of an electron from its innermost orbit. The atom is then left in an excited state. It is highly probable that an electron from the next orbit for which $n = 2$ may jump into the innermost orbit $n = 1$ and emit radiation of the frequency ν as noted in the foregoing equation. As for the factor $(Z - 1)$, since the innermost orbit normally contains two electrons, the remaining electron when one is removed has the effect of "screening" the Z positive charges of the nucleus. Therefore, when an electron moves from orbit $n = 2$ to orbit $n = 1$, it travels in an electric field resulting from Z positive charges and one negative charge, or $(Z - 1)$ positive charges.

It is also possible for an electron from orbit $n = 3$ to move into the orbit $n = 1$. When this occurs it gives rise to another line of the K series. Considering all the target atoms that have electrons knocked out of their innermost orbits, we find it more probable that an electron from orbit $n = 2$ will move into $n = 1$ than that an electron from $n = 3$ will move into the innermost orbit. This manifests itself in the greater intensity of the line resulting from the transition 2 to 1 than from the transition 3 to 1. The movement of an electron from $n = 4$ to $n = 1$ is also possible but not very likely. If it should occur, the line of the K series produced by this transition would be very weak.

X-RAY ENERGY LEVEL DIAGRAM

The interpretation of x-ray spectra is simplified by use of an energy-level diagram (Figure 5). Take the normal atom with its electrons in their normal state as the zero level of energy. When an electron is knocked out of the innermost orbit, it takes a specific amount of energy to acomplish this. Suppose that we represent this amount of energy by $\mathscr{E}_K$ and say that the atom is in the K state. But should an electron from orbit $n = 2$ be removed, then a smaller quantity of energy would be needed, $\mathscr{E}_L$, with the atom now in the L state. Similarly for electrons from $n = 3$ and $n = 4$. All these energy states are plotted in the x-ray energy level diagram.

Now suppose that an atom has been raised to the K state by the removal of an electron from the innermost orbit. If an electron moves from orbit $n = 2$ to the orbit $n = 1$, the atom will shift to the L state and radiation of frequency

$$\nu = (\mathscr{E}_K - \mathscr{E}_L)/h$$

will be released and we shall call this radiation the K_α line. But if an electron from $n = 3$ should move to $n = 1$, the atom will shift from the K state to the M state with the release of radiation of frequency

$$\nu = (\mathscr{E}_K - \mathscr{E}_M)/h.$$

In the diagram, this is called the K_β line. The K_γ line will be emitted when an electron moves from $n = 4$ to $n = 1$ and the atom changes from the K to the N state.

If an atom is in the L state because of an ejection of an electron from orbit $n = 2$ or because of the transition of an electron from 2 to 1, an electron from another orbit will move to $n = 2$ with an emission of a line of the L series. The frequency of each of these lines may be expressed by the same type of formula first introduced by Bohr in his theory of the hydrogen atom.

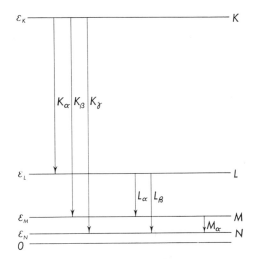

Figure 5 Simplified x-ray energy level diagram.

Advances in the study of x-ray spectra resulting in large part from the improvement in the precision and resolving power of the instruments used, and from the amount of energy available from improved types of x-ray tubes, show that many of the lines have two or more components. The simple energy-level diagram (Figure 5) must obviously be modified, chiefly by introduction of more energy levels close to some of those existing.

There is another method of studying the electronic structure of the atom that is more instructive. This makes use of x-rays from an external source striking the element under investigation. We may expect these x-rays to behave just like any other forms of radiation that strike matter; they will knock electrons out of an atom. This is the *photoelectric effect* with x-rays. There are two general methods for studying this phenomenon: one is to study the x-rays after they have traversed a known thickness of an element; the other is to study the electrons ejected from the element as a result of the action of the x-rays.

THE PHOTOELECTRIC EFFECT WITH X-RAYS

A simple type of experiment employing a device known as an *electron magnetic spectrograph* (Figure 6) helps us find the amount of energies in the electrons ejected from atoms by x-ray action. This kind of spectrograph is used widely for measuring

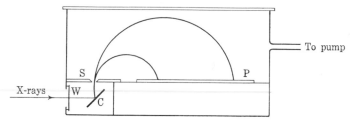

Figure 6   Magnetic spectrograph for determining the atomic energy levels.

the velocity of electrons. In this particular design of magnetic spectograph, x-rays of given frequency enter the apparatus through a window W and strike the substance under investigation at C. The electrons ejected as a result travel in all directions. Some pass through a narrow slit S into the upper region of the chamber. The whole chamber exists in a uniform magnetic field which has a direction at right angles to the plane of the diagram. The magnetic field forces the electrons to travel in circular paths and strike the photographic plate P. By using a vacuum pump to maintain as high a vacuum as possible in the spectograph, we are able to prevent loss of energy by the electrons.

The radius of a charged particle moving in a magnetic field of known strength is determined by the speed, mass, and charge of the particle. As electrons all have the same charge, the magnetic spectograph actually measures the momentum of the particle. That momentum, the mass multiplied by the speed, may be written as mv. When the masses are the same, the radius of the particle's path is proportionate to the speed of the particle. The radius of the path of the electron in this experiment can be measured from its position on the photographic plate; then its kinetic energy, $\frac{1}{2} mv^2$, can be calculated.

In general, when x-rays of frequency ν strike an element mounted at C, electrons of several different velocities, and therefore of several different energies, are recorded on the photographic plate. If an electron is removed from the K level, for example, its kinetic energy should be, from the photoelectric equation

$$\tfrac{1}{2}mv^2 = h\nu - \mathcal{E}_K.$$

From this the value of $\mathcal{E}_K$ may be ascertained. Values for other atomic energy levels have been obtained in this way for many elements.

ABSORPTION OF X-RAYS BY MATTER

One of the earliest observations on the properties of x-rays in the experiments leading to their discovery was that radiations could pass through matter opaque to visible radiation. The intensity of the x-rays after passage through a substance, however, is less than the intensity of the original beam. Figure 7 shows graphically the decrease in intensity of a beam of x-rays in terms of the distance it travels in a homogeneous substance.

The curve on the graph is known as an *exponential curve*. It is typical for all kinds of electromagnetic radiation. Distances along the x-axis are plotted in terms of distance D, called the *half-value thickness*; that is, the thickness of a substance that reduces the intensity of a beam passing through it to one-half its initial value. For a specific wavelength of x-rays, the half-value thickness is considerably smaller for lead than for aluminum or air. Thus a given thickness of lead will shield persons and instruments against exposure to x-rays better than less dense substances.

Another way of describing the absorption of x-rays is in terms of a *linear absorption coefficient*. This is the fractional decrease in the intensity of the beam per unit length of absorbing material. For a given type of x-rays, therefore, the linear absorption coefficient of lead is much greater than that of aluminum or air.

It is natural to ask what processes occur in the substance

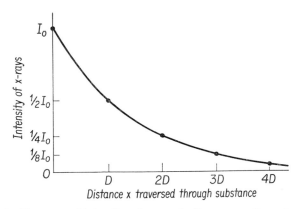

Figure 7   Decrease of intensity of x-rays in its passage through matter.

to cut the intensity of the x-ray beam as it passes through this material. We have already examined one of these processes, the photoelectric effect with x-rays. Here the striking rays, considered as photons of energy, eject electrons from their normal positions in atoms, giving up *all* their energies in the process. The energy of the photon is shared by the electron and the atom, some of it as the kinetic energy of the liberated electron and the rest as potential energy of the atom.

As we have seen, the atom can return to its normal state when outer electrons move to vacated inner levels inciting emission of radiation characteristic of the atom. When x-rays are emitted by atoms that have been excited by radiation, the emitted radiation is sometimes called *fluorescent radiation*.

THE SCATTERING OF X-RAYS

Another process for removing energy from the incident beam is one in which the substance *scatters* some of the energy in all directions. The scattering is produced by the electrons of the substance. J. J. Thomson has developed a theory to account for this by assuming that the incident radiation accelerates the electrons. As we have seen, the accelerated electrons then emit electromagnetic radiations of the same frequency as the incident radiation. Thomson's theory, also called the classical theory, of the scattering of x-rays, leads to three conclusions that can be checked by experiment.

1. The rate at which energy is scattered by a given amount of an element is proportional to the number of electrons present. By knowing the density of the substance and its atomic number, the number of electrons per atom can be calculated. This was done by Barkla in 1911 and repeated with greater accuracy by Hewlett in 1922 using a block of carbon as the scattering substance. They found that there were six electrons in every atom of carbon—the same as the atomic number of carbon—effective in scattering. This was direct evidence that the atomic number was equal to the number of electrons in the atom.

2. X-rays scattered at 90° to the incident rays should be polarized just as visible light is polarized by scattering from fine particles. This was first verified experimentally by Barkla who

thus demonstrated that x-rays were transverse waves exactly like light waves.

3. The intensity of x-rays scattered through different angles with respect to the original beam is calculated as a function of the angle of scattering. The experimental results agree with the theory for x-ray wavelengths greater than 0.2A but differ markedly from the theoretical predictions when shorter wavelengths are scattered. Evidently the Thomson theory of scattering is not entirely satisfactory. To account for the discrepancy occurring with the use of short wavelength x-rays, Arthur Holly Compton proposed a *quantum theory* of scattering in 1923. In Compton's theory, the x-ray beam is considered to consist of photons which collide with electrons and eject them from the atom with a certain amount of kinetic energy. The photons themselves are then scattered with reduced energy. This theory succeeds in predicting the correct intensity distribution and the correct change in wavelength of the scattered radiation. We shall examine this in some detail in the next chapter.

9 WAVES AND PARTICLES

THE DUAL CHARACTER OF RADIATION

For three centuries the fundamental nature of light has been a topic of controversy. Sir Isaac Newton advanced the hypothesis that light consisted of a stream of particles moving with high speed through a given medium. Newton assigned to these particles properties needed to explain the phenomena known at the time. Christian Huygens, a contemporary of Newton, maintained that light was propagated as a wave in an elastic medium. By the beginning of the nineteenth century, the Newtonian hypothesis had been favored for about 150 years. Then, numerous experiments on *interference* and *diffraction* brought about a shift in support to the wave theory advocated by Huygens.

Originally, Huygens thought that light waves were transverse waves in the elastic medium. After the electromagnetic theory of light was developed by James Clerk Maxwell in 1865 and supported by Heinrich Hertz's experimental evidence twenty-two years later, physicists accepted the view that light was propagated as an electromagnetic wave. Electromagnetic waves—or electromagnetic radiation—became the classification for describing both visible radiation and invisible radiation, including the longer waves of infrared and radio, and the shorter waves of ultraviolet light, x-rays, and gamma rays from radioactive substances.

Development of the electromagnetic theory of radiation has been one of the outstanding achievements of the past hundred years. Nevertheless, difficulties soon started to appear in efforts to explain some phenomena that may be regarded as the interaction of radiation with matter. Some of these difficulties were overcome in 1900 by Planck's concept of a *quantum of energy* which made clear the distribution of energy in *black body* radiation. According to the Planck hypothesis, energy is emitted or absorbed in whole *quanta* whenever radiation is emitted or absorbed by a black body at a certain temperature. Expressed algebraically, a *quantum of energy* is

$$\mathcal{E} = h\nu \, .$$

In 1905, as we have seen, Einstein drew on the Planck concept to explain the photoelectric effect, in which a quantum of radiation called a photon yields all its energy in ejecting an electron from an atomic system or a metallic surface. We have also seen that an extension of this idea was made in 1913 by Niels Bohr. Bohr added the fundamental notion that the energy of an atomic system in changing from an initial value $\mathcal{E}_i$ to a final value $\mathcal{E}_f$ does so with the emission or absorption of a quantum of radiation.

Electromagnetic radiation thus began to acquire a dual nature. It was a wave and a particle, at the same time.

THE COMPTON EFFECT

One of the most significant phenomena disclosing the particle, or corpuscular, nature of radiation is the *Compton effect* with x-rays. This phenomenon is treated as a collision of two particles, a photon and an electron. The treatment combines the quantum idea of radiation with the relativistic concepts of mass and energy.

Imagine an x-ray photon of frequency ν and energy $h\nu$ colliding with an electron initially at rest (Figure 1). Instead of relinquishing all its energy to the electron, the photon sets the electron in motion at angle θ while itself being scattered in a direction that forms angle ϕ with its original own direction of motion. If the electron's mass is m_e and it is given a velocity v, the electron acquires kinetic energy $\frac{1}{2}m_ev^2$ as the result of the collision. The scattered photon loses energy in the action; after the collision, its energy becomes $h\nu'$ so that

$$h\nu - h\nu' = \tfrac{1}{2}m_ev^2.$$

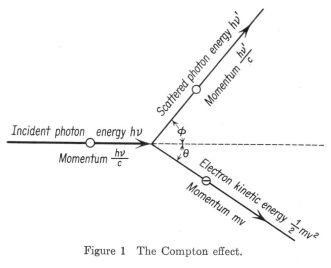

Figure 1   The Compton effect.

The frequency of the scattered photon, it will be seen, is less than the frequency of the incident photon.

The change of frequency because of scattering depends on the angle of the scattering. To prove this, we must apply the principle of conservation of momentum to this process.

The momentum of a particle is the product of its mass and velocity. The momentum of the electron in this case is $m_e v$; it is a vector in the direction of the velocity. Now the momentum of a photon can also be expressed as the product of its mass and velocity. We know from the Einstein special theory of relativity that the mass of a photon is its energy divided by the square of the speed of light. The mass of the photon prior to scattering is thus $h\nu/c^2$, but after scattering $h\nu'/c^2$. The respective momenta of these particles are $h\nu/c$ and $h\nu'/c$.

The original equation may now be solved, subject to the condition that the momentum of the incident photon equals the sum of the momenta of the scattered photon and the electron. In terms of corresponding wavelengths λ and λ' of the incident and scattered rays the solution is

$$\lambda' - \lambda = \frac{h}{m_e c}\,(1 - \text{cosine } \phi)$$

with ϕ the symbol for the angle of scattering.

The change in wavelength predicted by the Compton effect has been measured in many experiments and the results have been found to agree with the foregoing equation. When the angle of scattering is 90° the value of cosine $\phi = 0$ and the change in wavelength of the radiation becomes $h/m_e c$. This quantity is sometimes called the Compton wavelength and has a value of 0.024A.

The energy and momentum of the scattered, or *recoil*, electron have also been checked by experiment and been found to agree with the results predicted by the Compton theory.

DE BROGLIE'S HYPOTHESIS

The dual character, wave and particle, of radiation is definitely established by the experiments we have described. There is no reason to insist that it bo ono or tho othor; it can exhibit either aspect, wave or particle, depending on the type of experiment under way. Moreover, quantities such as wavelength and frequency, emerging from its wave character, are used to describe its mass and momentum, which are generally associated with particles.

Louis De Broglie, studying the dual character, took the next bold step. He contended that the duality should not be limited to radiation but should pertain to all matter including electrons, protons, neutrons, atoms, molecules, and even golf balls, among other things. In his experimentation, De Broglie appropriated those relationships found to be valid for the dual nature of radiation in order to assign a wavelength to waves related to matter. For example, the momentum p of a photon is expressed as

$$p = h\nu/c.$$

Since the wavelength λ is related to the frequency ν by the equation $\nu\lambda = c$, and

$$\lambda = c/\nu,$$

we can write

$$p = h/\lambda$$

or

$$\lambda = h/p$$

as the fundamental relationship between momentum and wavelength, with h as the Planck constant.

De Broglie's hypothesis is that a wave is associated with every particle, and the wavelength of this wave can be written as

$$\lambda = h/mv.$$

In this case, mv represents the momentum of a particle of mass m and velocity v, and is equal to p.

The nature of this wave associated with a material particle has not been specified; it still remains to be determined. The velocity w of this wave differs from the velocity v of the particle and from the speed of light c. But the three velocities are closely related by the equation

$$vw = c^2.$$

Since the speed of a material particle is always less than the speed of light, the wave velocity is greater than the velocity of light. This does not contradict any deductions or conclusions arising from the theory of relativity as the energy carried by a particle moves with the velocity v which is always less than c.

WAVES ASSOCIATED WITH MATTER

The only acceptable proof of the existence of a wave motion is the appearance of *interference* and *diffraction* phenomena. Not long after De Broglie announced his hypothesis, two successful experiments pushed his thinking further. They showed the existence of waves connected with electrons.

In the first of these experiments, Davisson and Germer reflected electrons from a nickel crystal (Figure 2a) and obtained an intense maximum at an angle fitting the Bragg equation (page 100) originally developed for x-rays (Figure 2b). The wavelength of the waves associated with the electrons, determined from the Bragg equation, agreed with the wavelength calculated from the De Broglie equation. For example, electrons with an energy of 100 ev, according to De Broglie's equation have a wavelength of 1.22A. This value agrees with that found by experiment.

In the second experiment, G. P. Thomson demonstrated the existence of electron waves in another way. He allowed a thin pencil of electrons or cathode rays to pass through a metallic foil (Figure 3) and strike a photographic plate. Ordinary metals such as aluminum, silver, and gold consist of a large number of

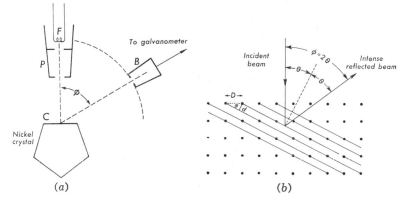

(a)   (b)

Figure 2   (a) Outline of the experimental arrangement in the electron diffraction experiment of Davisson and Germer. (b) Diffraction of electron beam by atomic planes of a crystal is treated in the same manner as x-ray diffraction.

tiny crystals oriented at random. Quite probably some of these crystals are oriented at the proper angle to give a Bragg type of reflection of the waves associated with the electrons. Since the crystals in the selected metal were oriented at random, the diffraction pattern on the photographic plate was circular. Figure 4 shows a diffraction pattern, made more recently than the Thomson experiment, resulting from the passage of a stream of electrons through a film of gold.

Diffraction and interference patterns have also been obtained from waves associated with protons, neutrons, helium atoms, and

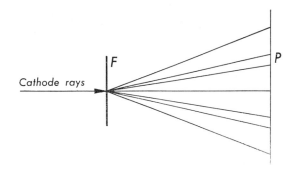

Figure 3 Schematic diagram of electron diffraction experiments of G. P. Thomson.

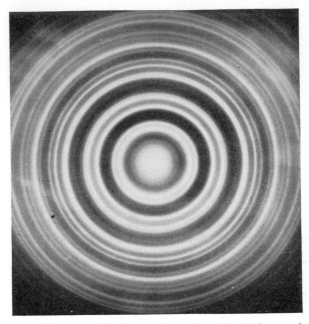

Figure 4   Electron diffraction pattern of gold; thickness of the gold film was about 250 A. (*From photograph by Oliver Row and N. R. Mukherjee.*)

hydrogen molecules. Matter waves—or De Broglie waves, as they are often called—are now as common and accepted as x-rays and light.

HEISENBERG'S "UNCERTAINTY PRINCIPLE"

The German physicist Werner Heisenberg has provided an interesting interpretation of the wave and particle duality of matter and radiant energy. The concepts of particle and wave have been developed through experiments performed on a comparatively large scale; the concepts themselves are mental images formed on the basis of these experiments. Applied to experiments involving the smaller quantities of atomic dimensions, these concepts can have only the validity of analogies. The concept of the electron as a particle, for example, derives from results of experiments on the motion of an electron through electric and magnetic fields. The problem is to predict the position and velocity of the particle at any time when its initial position and velocity are known. But experiments on the diffraction of electrons demonstrate that this is not always possible.

Electrons starting with the same conditions are not all scattered through the same angle by the crystals. The resulting diffraction pattern shows a definite distribution of the electrons with respect to position and momentum. But a diffraction pattern provides the best evidence that we have of a wave phenomenon. Applying this to a single electron, the electron may be imagined as a small bundle or packet of waves stretching over some small region of space designated as Δs. The association of a wave packet with an electron means that the position of the electron at any instant of time cannot be specified with any pinpointed accuracy. All we can say of the electron is that it is somewhere within the group of waves extending over the space Δs.

Heisenberg's *uncertainty principle* refers to the simultaneous determination of the position and momentum of the particle. It states that the uncertainty Δx in the measurement of the position of the particle and the uncertainty Δp_x in the simultaneous measurement of its momentum are governed by the relationship

$$\Delta x \cdot \Delta p_x \geqslant h.$$

Niels Bohr has suggested an idealized experiment that shows how the wave concept serves as a limitation on the particle concept, thus giving rise to the uncertainty principle. Suppose that we wish to find the position of an electron by using some instrument such as a microscope of high power. The power of the microscope, as expressed mathematically, is

$$\Delta x = \lambda / sin a$$

with Δx representing the distance between two separate distinguishable points, λ the wavelength of the light used for viewing, and a the semivertical angle of the cone of light from the illuminated object (Figure 5).

The uncertainty in finding the exact position of the electron is thus Δx. To make the uncertainty as small as possible, light of very short wavelength should be used. This suggests the use of x-rays. The minimum amount of light required for illuminating the electron is a single photon of energy $h\nu$ and momentum h/λ. If the photon approaches from the left, it must be scattered by

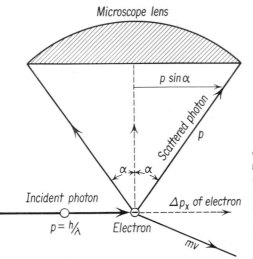

Figure **5** Schematic diagram of x-ray microscope experiment. Incident photon scattered into lens may enter along any direction making an angle between zero and alpha with the axis of the lens.

the electron into the microscope (Figure 5). This is merely the Compton effect; the electron receives some momentum from the photon.

We can obtain this momentum from the equations of the Compton effect if we know the angle through which the x-ray photon has been scattered. The photon may enter the microscope through any one of a large range of angles. The spread of values of the x-component of the scattered photon's momentum varies from zero to $\dfrac{h}{\lambda}$ sinα and the uncertainty in the x-component of the electron's momentum is expressed as

$$\Delta p_x = \frac{h}{\lambda}\sin\alpha.$$

The product of the uncertainties in the simultaneous determinations of the position and momentum of the electron may be written

$$\Delta x \cdot \Delta p_x = \frac{\lambda}{\sin\alpha} \times \frac{h\sin\alpha}{\lambda} = h.$$

ELECTRON OPTICS

Nearly all the phenomena usually associated with light and x-rays, and which form the subject of optics, can also be observed with electrons. Electrons can be reflected and refracted. Interference and diffraction effects can be produced at will. Electrons from a source may be focused by passing them through properly shaped electric or magnetic fields—fields that play the role of lenses. In fact, within recent years, a completely new branch of science, known as *electron optics*, has been developed and investigations in this area not only have led to improved understanding of physical phenomena but they have also produced several important instruments which have broad applications. One of these is the *electron microscope.*

A microscope provides a magnified image of a small object and shows greater detail in the object's structure. The degree of detail seen is determined by the resolving power of the microscope. We know already that the resolving power of a microscope has as its limit the wavelength of the incident radiation. In the case of optical microscopes, the limit of the resolving power is the wavelength of visible light, about 5,000A. But as the wavelengths associated with electrons are ascertained from the formula

$$\lambda = h/mv,$$

it is possible to produce much smaller wavelengths through use of appropriate accelerating voltages on the electrons and thereby obtain microscopes with much higher resolving power. Electron microscopes have been produced with resolving powers of about 20A by using accelerating voltages from 30 kv to 100 kv.

Figure 6 shows a simplified cross section of a compact, high-resolving-power electron microscope. This microscope uses magnetic fields for both its objective and projection lenses. Either an electromagnet or a permanent magnet may be used. The specimen to be studied has to be very thin so that electrons of about 30 kev energy can be transmitted through it without any loss of energy. The instrument is so designed that the image can be focused on a fluorescent screen for examination, and it is also constructed to permit the placement of a photographic plate in front of the screen for photographing the image. A diffusion pump connected to the microscope provides the vacuum.

This instrument can be provided also with an adapter for use as an electron diffraction camera. Other electron microscopes have been designed for the study of the surfaces of thick materials by the reflection of electrons from the surface. The development of

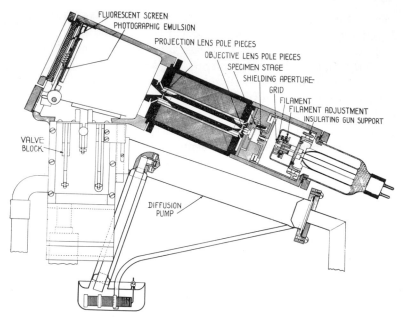

Figure 6   A simplified cross section of a small electron microscope. (*Courtesy of RCA Laboratories.*)

these electron microscopes has made available a powerful tool for the study of the structure of large molecules, the structure of bacteria, the photographs of viruses, and other infinitesmal objects.

WAVE MECHANICS; PROBABILITY CONCEPTS

The fundamental ideas of De Broglie were drawn upon in 1926 by Schroedinger for a new formulation of mechanics dealing with atomic particles. Schroedinger's method consisted of incorporating waves associated with particles into equations analogous to the wave equations used to solve problems of electromagnetic radiation. The subject has come to be known as *wave mechanics*.

At about the same time Heisenberg and Dirac, independently of one another, perfected methods for coping with the mechanics of atomic systems. Their researches complemented Schroedinger's method. One of the beneficial by-products of all these studies has been the growing use of the concept of probability in interpretations of atomic phenomena.

For example, if a beam of light passes through a narrow slit and strikes a photographic plate, a definite diffraction pattern results showing an alternation of regions of great and small intensity. Interpreted statistically, the probability of a photon striking the photographic plate is great when the intensity is great and small when the intensity is small. In the case of a weak beam of light—say, one in which a single photon passes through the slit every minute—it is impossible to predict just where any individual photon will hit the plate. All we know is that the probability of the photon striking a particular portion of the plate is large where the wave theory predicts large intensity and small where the wave theory predicts small intensity. If only a few photons strike the photographic plate, their arrangement is likely to be haphazard. But if a sufficient time is permitted to elapse so that a large number of photons reaches the plate, the diffraction pattern predicted by the wave theory results.

The foregoing mode of description applies to the diffraction of an electron beam by a narrow slit. The wave associated with the electron is the De Broglie wave. There is a certain probability that an electron after passing through the slit will strike a fixed point on the photographic plate; this probability is proportional to the square of the amplitude of the De Broglie wave. Although, as with the photon, we cannot predict where any one electron will strike, a definite diffraction pattern can be seen and the intensities at different points will correspond to the amplitudes of the diffracted waves at those points when there is a sufficient interval of time to permit a large number of electrons to strike the photographic plate.

The phenomenon of transmission and reflection at a plane surface responds to similar explanation. If a system of waves strikes a plane surface, part of it will be reflected and part transmitted, and its intensities will be in proportion to the squares of the amplitudes of the reflected and transmitted waves, respectively. In terms of corpuscular theory, the particle associated with the incident wave has a certain probability of being reflected and a certain probability of being transmitted; the probabilities are in proportion to the squares of the amplitudes of the corresponding waves.

From this discussion, as developed in the last two sections of this chapter, we can assert that although there may be an indeterminacy in the description of phenomena from the corpuscular point of view, no such lack of determinacy exists from the point of view of the wave theory.

10 THE SOLID STATE

CRYSTALLINE STRUCTURE

The atom is the primary interest of this book. We are concerned in particular with its structure, its properties, and its behavior under the influence of various kinds of forces. Rarely is an atom wholly free from the actions of other atoms and it is to an understanding of the nature and extent of these effects that many of the experiments we have described are directed. Let us turn attention to the solids.

Atoms of the same or different type often combine to form molecules. These atoms are held together by short-range forces because of the atoms' electrical charges. When atoms or molecules of any substance exist in a solid state, the forces binding them together make them form geometrical patterns which show up as a *crystalline structure*. Sometimes these crystals grow to large

Figure 1   Photograph of a large quartz crystal grown at the Bell Telephone Laboratories. (*Courtesy of Bell Telephone Laboratories.*)

size and are then called *single crystals*; rock salt, calcite, and
quartz are often found as such (Figure 1). The structure of a
single crystal may be ascertained with the aid of x-rays by using
either a Bragg-type, single-crystal spectrometer or a Laue diffraction type.

Actually most crystals are imperceptible to the naked eye.
They can be seen only with the help of a microscope. Most metals
are composed of these small crystals, or *microcrystals*. These
microcrystals can be studied through electron diffraction by pre-
paring thin films of the metal containing them. Their structure
and composition may also be investigated through use of the
x-ray powder diffraction method.

X-RAY POWDER DIFFRACTION

The ordinary solid is composed of many microcrystals. Even
in powder form, this is generally so. We are able to analyze the
structures of these microcrystals by applying x-rays to them in
a method devised by A. W. Hull, and independently by P. Debye
and P. Scherrer.

The method consists of sending a narrow pencil of x-rays
through a tiny sample of the powder or solid (Figure 2). The
x-rays may be of a single wavelength or a few known wavelengths. It is probable that since the powder or solid contains
many microcrystals set at random one of them will be oriented
in a way that enables its atomic plane to form an angle θ with
the incident radiation. This will meet the requirements of the
Bragg equation for the wavelength of the incident rays. It is

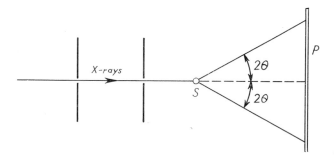

Figure 2   Method of obtaining x-ray diffraction patterns using a powder at *S*.

Figure 3 X-ray powder diffraction pattern of aluminium. (*Reproduced with the permission of A. W. Hull.*)

likely also that the atomic planes of other microcrystals in the powder or solid will make the same angle with the incident rays but in different planes of incidence. In each case, the angle between the original beam and the reflected beam will be 2θ. A photographic plate, perpendicular to the original beam at a convenient distance from the sample, will record the diffraction pattern. This pattern will consist of a series of circles (Figure 3), each of which is an intersection of the cone of the central angle 4θ and the plane of the photographic plate. The radius of the circle is determined by the distance of the plate from the sample, the wavelength of the incident rays, the size of the diffraction, and the grating space of the crystal.

In a variation of this method, a photographic film replaces the plate. The film is bent in the form of a cylinder with the sample at its center. Holes are punctured in the film to permit the x-rays to enter and leave without blackening the film. When the film is unrolled and developed, a pattern is evident (Figure 4). This method, in the original or modification, is capable of very high precision. Called the x-ray powder diffraction method, it is receiving extensive usage.

W Powder

Figure 4 X-ray powder diffraction pattern of tungsten obtained with a film bent in the form of a circular cylinder. (*From a photograph made by L. L. Wyman and supplied by A. W. Hull.*)

CONDUCTORS; CONDUCTION ELECTRONS

Electrons of an isolated atom have specific levels of energy. But when several atoms form a solid, the electrons of one are affected by forces from the electrons of its neighbors, and this causes some of the energy levels to become diffuse and even overlap each other. The innermost electrons forming the core of the atom suffer little effect while the outermost electrons experience the greatest disturbance. In a metallic solid, some of the outer electrons drift freely from one atom to another; these are the *conduction electrons.*

The distribution of energies among conduction electrons depends on the temperature of the metal in which they reside. At absolute zero, 0° K, the conduction electrons have a wide range of energies. The energy distribution of these electrons, (Figure 5) is based on a statistical theory developed by Fermi and Dirac. The number of electrons within a given energy range is plotted against the energy. For 0° K, the theory predicts that the energy distribution will spread from zero to maximum energy $\mathcal{E}_m$, a quantity determined by the number of conduction electrons in each unit volume of the metal. When the metal is heated, the distribution changes slightly for the electrons in the upper energy levels; this is illustrated in the graph for a temperature of 1500° K, which is 1227° centigrade. The increase in energies for these electrons at high temperature makes possible the evaporation of some of the electrons from the surface of the metal. Thus we get the thermionic effect (page 17).

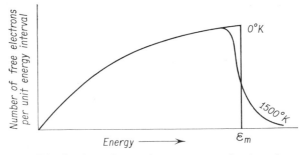

Figure 5 Distribution of energies among conduction electrons of a metal at 0°K and 1500°K.

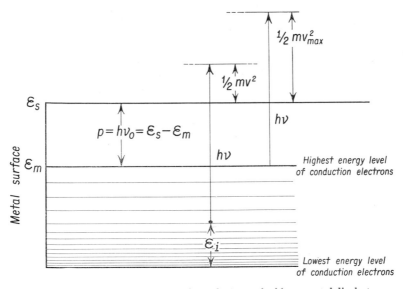

Figure 6 Energies of conduction electrons inside a metal lie between 0 and $\mathcal{E}_m$. The kinetic energy with which an electron is ejected by a photon depends upon its energy level in the metal.

Figure 6 diagrams the relationship between the energy band of the conduction electrons and the energy $\mathcal{E}_s$ needed to remove an electron from the zero level through the surface of the metal when the temperature is 0° K. It takes an amount $\mathcal{E}_s - \mathcal{E}_m$ to remove an electron from the highest level through the surface.

The energy for removing the electron may come from heating the metal, as in the thermionic effect, or from radiation, as in the photoelectric effect. If a photon of energy $h\nu$, therefore, precipitates the ejection of an electron having an initial energy $\mathcal{E}_i$, it will emerge with some value of kinetic energy $\frac{1}{2}mv^2$. If the ejected electron comes from the highest level, it will leave the surface with maximum kinetic energy. The minimum amount of energy it takes for a photon to remove an electron from a metal at 0° K is found from the equation

$$p = h\nu_0 = \mathcal{E}_s - \mathcal{E}_m$$

in which p signifies the threshold energy and ν_0 the threshold frequency.

At room temperature, about 300° K, the energy distribution among the conduction electrons does not differ significantly from the pattern at 0° K. This accounts for the fact that an upper limit exists to the kinetic energy of the photoelectrons from metallic surfaces at ordinary temperatures.

SEMICONDUCTORS; TRANSISTORS

The increase in knowledge of the electronic structure of atoms and in particular of the way in which atoms group into crystals has lead to the development of certain semiconductors that can take the place of the three-element thermionic tube. Silicon and germanium are both prime examples of this advance. Used this way, such a crystal is known as a *transistor*.

The interesting properties of crystals employed as transistors depend upon the presence of minute amounts of impurities in the crystals. These impurities, moreover, can be introduced in exact amounts to achieve the results desired. For example, atoms of germanium each contain four outer electrons which they share among each other in the crystal. But if one atom of antimony, Sb, which has five outer electrons, replaces one atom of germanium, one excess electron will occupy the region. This electron may be set in motion by application of a small electric field. A germanium crystal having this kind of impurity is called an n-type crystal, with n symbolizing negative charge. On the other hand, if an atom of indium, In, with only three outer electrons, were to replace a germanium atom, there would be a deficiency of electrons, a "hole" left in this part of the crystal. When an electric field is applied in this type of situation, electrons from other parts of the crystal flow toward the holes, leaving deficiencies elsewhere in the crystal and the current may be regarded as the motion of these holes. A hole in a region that is normally occupied by an electron is equivalent to the presence of a positive charge at this point. A germanium crystal with this kind of impurity which produces the holes is a p-type crystal, with p representing positive charge.

A transistor has either two p-type regions separated by an n-type region or it may have two n-type regions separated by a p-type. The former is known as a p-n-p transistor, the latter as an n-p-n transistor. Figure 7 diagrams an n-p-n transistor.

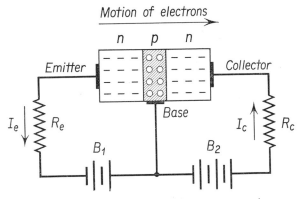

Figure 7   Schematic diagram of an n-p-n transistor.

The electrode connected to the p-region is called the *base*, one wire or electrode connected to an n-region is called the *emitter*, and the other wire or electrode is called the *collector*.

A transistor functions as a power amplifier. Its action may be demonstrated by connecting one battery B_1 so that the base becomes positive in relation to the emitter while a second battery B_2 puts an opposite bias on the collector. The electric field in the left half of the crystal is directed to push electrons and holes to a junction and electrons into and through the p-region. The conductivity of the crystal is thus large for current in this direction. If the terminals of B_1 were reversed, the electrons and holes would be pushed away from the junction, and the conductivity would become small as a result. The crystal thus has a low resistance for current in one direction and a high resistance for current in the opposite direction.

The collector region has a high resistance when the emitter region has a low one. If the thickness of the p-region is small, many electrons from the n-region on the left will pass through the p-region to the n-region on the right and move toward the collector. There will also be a small current resulting from the motion of electrons and holes of the region on the right.

If we call the current in the emitter branch I_e, and the resistance of the branch R_e, the power developed in it is $I_e^2 R_e$. Similarly, the power developed in the collector branch is $I_c^2 R_c$. The value of R_c is usually considerably greater than R_e because of the way the electric fields produced by the batteries are biased in the different sections of the crystal. The ratio of power delivered to the collector to that in the emitter is

$$\frac{I_c^2 \, R_c}{I_e^2 \, R_e}.$$

Even though I_c is only slightly greater than I_e, the power gain may be as much as 100,000 units.

Transistors are quite small in size. The largest dimension is generally less than one inch. They are rapidly replacing thermionic tubes in many different types of circuits. One of the main advantages of a transistor is its low power requirements, chiefly because no heating elements are needed to supply electrons as with thermionic tubes. Transistors have also been developed with four electrodes, corresponding to the four-element thermionic tube.

11 NATURAL RADIOACTIVITY

Knowledge has its own chain reaction. The discovery of one important phenomenon usually leads to another. In 1895, Roentgen discovered x-rays; this set the stage for Becquerel's discovery of radioactivity a year later. Becquerel sought to find out whether there was any connection between the fluorescence of the glass of an x-ray tube and the phosphorescence of certain salts when irradiated by ordinary light.

To pursue his investigations, he turned to a double sulphate of uranium and potassium. First he wrapped a photographic plate in thick black paper and placed a crystal of uranium salt on top

Figure 1 Henri Becquerel (1852–1908). Discovered phenomenon of radioactivity. (*Courtesy of Culver Service.*)

of the paper. Then he exposed the whole package to sunlight. On developing the plate, he found a silhouette of the salt crystal on the negative and surmised that this had been produced by radiations emanating from the crystal.

He followed up this experiment with others in which he inserted various absorbing materials between the uranium salt and the photographic plate. In each case, he found the same thing: when he developed the plate, he noticed the shadow of the absorbing material on the plate. This he believed to be caused by the absorption of radiation by the substance placed between the uranium salt and the photographic plate. The crowning experiment was one in which he decided against irradiating the salt with light from an external source, but chose instead to investigate whether the salt itself might be a source of radiations.

For these experiments, Becquerel built a lightproof box with the photographic plate placed at the bottom. In one test, he placed uranium salt crystals on the plate. The developed plate showed silhouettes of the individual crystals. In another experiment, he inserted a piece of aluminum between the crystals and the photographic plate; again he found the silhouettes of the crystals on the developed plate, but this time they had less intensity because the aluminum had absorbed some of the radiations. From all these experiments, Becquerel concluded that the radiations came from the uranium salt, irrespective of the impact of external light on them.

Becquerel then continued with a series of investigations to find the origin of these radiations. Using a variety of compounds of uranium in his studies, he concluded that the radiations were emitted by the uranium in the compounds. Some of the compounds were phosphorescent; others were not. He also discovered an important aspect of these radiations: they could touch off the discharge of electrically charged bodies. This made it possible to check the phenomenon quantitatively with the help of ionization chambers and electroscopes, or electrometers.

Not long after, Ernest Rutherford studied the penetrating power of the radiation from uranium salt by measuring the ionization it produced in an ionization chamber. He found that the radiation consisted of two parts: a very soft part easily absorbed in matter, which he called *alpha rays*, and a more penetrating part, which he called *beta rays*. The radiation that oper-

Figure 2   Marie Curie (1867–1934) and Pierre Curie (1859–1906). Discovered two new radioactive elements, polonium and radium. Mme. Curie continued as a leader in the field of radioactivity throughout her life. Pierre Curie had previously made some important contributions to the subject of magnetism. (*Courtesy of Culver Service.*)

ated in the Becquerel experiments is now known to have consisted of beta rays.

By an ionization method, Mme. Marie Curie further showed that the activity of the uranium salt was in proportion to the mass of uranium in the salt. In this way, she demonstrated the atomic nature of radioactivity. She and her husband, Pierre Curie, then subjected uranium pitchblende to a systematic chemical analysis and, again with an electrical method, measured the activity of the elements obtained from the mineral. In 1898, they succeeded in discovering two new radioactive elements, polonium and radium. Their work won them a joint Nobel prize.

Radium was precipitated by the Curies as a salt in the form of radium chloride. They found its activity to be more than a million times greater than an equal mass of uranium. Pure radium metal was first obtained in 1910 by decomposing the fused salt. Its atomic weight was found to be 226.05. It fitted in at the end of the second group in the periodic table (page 3); in chemical structure, it was similar to calcium, strontium, and barium. Many more radioactive substances have since been discovered, filling many of the gaps which existed in the periodic table before Becquerel's discovery of radioactivity.

In addition to alpha and beta rays, naturally radioactive substances emit a third type of radiation—*gamma rays*. The existence of these three kinds of radiations may be demonstrated very simply. A small amount of some radioactive salt is placed at the bottom of a long, narrow groove in a block of lead (Figure 3). Through slit S comes an almost parallel beam from the radioactive substance R; rays moving in other directions are absorbed by the block. The block itself is encased in an air-tight chamber containing a photographic plate P above the slit. To avoid absorption of the rays the air is pumped out of the chamber. A strong magnetic field is applied at right angles to the plane of the book page and directed away from the reader.

After a reasonable interval of exposure, three distinct lines may be found on the developed photographic plate. The line deflected to the left is produced by alpha rays, composed of a stream of positively charged particles called *alpha particles*. The line deflected to the right is produced by beta rays, made up of a stream of negatively charged particles called *beta particles*. The undeviated third line results from gamma radiation, which is unaffected by a magnetic field. The line's direction, therefore, must be attributed either to a stream of neutral particles or to a beam of electromagnetic radiation. Experiments on interference and diffraction of the gamma rays, similar to those performed

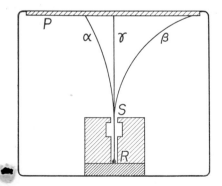

Figure 3 Paths of the rays from a radioactive substance R in a magnetic field. The magnetic field is perpendicular to the plane of the paper and directed into the paper.

with x-rays, indicate that gamma rays are electromagnetic radiations of extremely short wavelengths of approximately 0.1A or less.

Studies show that some naturally radioactive elements emit alpha particles and others emit beta particles, and that gamma rays sometimes accompany the emission of either. After the Becquerel discovery of radioactivity, it was surmised that all these rays flow from the nucleus as a result of some spontaneous changes taking place in it. In view of this, if a nucleus emits a charged particle, its atomic number changes, and it must become the nucleus of a new type of atom. Chemistry plays an important part in following the changes. By allowing the disintegrations of a known radioactive element to continue for a while and then analyzing the substance again, we find many new elements formed in consequence of the disintegrations.

A careful study of the nature and properties of the rays emitted during the disintegrations, supplemented by chemical analysis of the substances, should yield valuable evidence on nuclear structure and the nuclear processes. In should also provide some guidance to the physicist on how to induce nuclear changes so as to make available to himself, the chemist, biologist, physician, and engineer many new atoms and atomic processes. This actually has been the history of radioactivity.

COUNTING ALPHA PARTICLES

Alpha rays, as we have said, consist of a stream of positively charged particles. The ratio of the charge q to the mass M of these particles may be obtained by measuring the deflections of the alpha rays in their passage through known electric and magnetic fields. Such measurements show that $q/M = 48{,}200$ coul/gm. If the charge could be determined independently, we could then calculate its mass. One way of finding the charge is by counting the number of alpha particles released by some radioactive element in a specific interval of time and then determining the total charge carried by these particles. This may be done in two different ways: either by the scintillation method or the Geiger-counter method.

In the scintillation method, alpha particles strike a fluorescent screen made of small crystals; these crystals convert the kinetic energy of the particles into visible radiation. In early experimental work, the screen was viewed through a low-powered microscope. A small crystal that was struck by an alpha particle emitted a brilliant flash of light which lasted only a very short time—hence the name *scintillation*. The microscope's field of view was made so small that not more than two to four scintillations could be seen per second thereby enabling the viewer to count them readily with a mechanical device. By knowing the area of the field of view and also the distance of the radioactive material from it, the viewer could calculate the number of alpha particles emitted by the radioactive substance in a given time period.

Development of the photomultiplier tubes (page 25) and appropriate electric circuits made possible the counting of scintillations via the photoelectric effect. Instruments based on this phenomenon are called *scintillation counters* and are now in wide use to count alpha particles and other radiations that can produce fluorescence in various types of transparent substances, whether these substances are in the liquid or solid phase.

In the Geiger-counter method, use is made of the fact that the alpha particle produces intense ionization along its path while passing through a gas. Many different types of counters are now obtainable. Essentially, a Geiger counter consists of a cylinder containing a fine wire mounted parallel to its axis and insulated from it (Figure 4). The cylinder contains a gas such as air or argon at a pressure between five and twelve cm of mercury. A difference of potential slightly less than is necessary to produce a discharge through the gas is maintained between the wire W

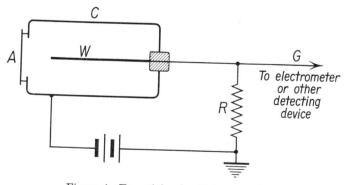

Figure 4   Essentials of a Geiger counter.

and the cylinder C. Alpha particles enter the counter through the aperture A, which may be covered by a thin sheet of mica, glass, or aluminum. A particle entering the counter ionizes the gas along its path. The ions formed by this action are accelerated by the electric field between the wire and the cylinder. These ions, in turn, produce more ions by collisions with the gas molecules and the ionization current builds up rapidly as a result. A high resistance R is connected between the wire and a grounding to dissipate the ionization current's energy at a rapid pace. In sum, a momentary current is produced; it may be registered on an electrometer connected at G, or it may be amplified by specially designed amplifiers and heard on a loudspeaker or recorded on a mechanical counter. By proper design of the cylinder and choice of resistance, the time required for dissipation of the momentary current may be made very short so that each alpha particle entering the counter can be registered.

The Geiger counter is named for its designer, a German physicist named Hans Geiger. He and Rutherford both found by using Geiger counters that one gram of radium in one second, for example, emits 3.57×10^{10} alpha particles. The present accepted value, however, is 3.70×10^{10} alpha particles per second from a gram of radium. This number has come to be called a *curie* after the discoverers of radium. As a unit of radioactivity the *curie* has now been extended to nuclear disintegration of all types and symbolizes the *disintegration of 3.70×10^{10} nuclei per second.*

NATURE OF THE ALPHA PARTICLE

Investigation has shown conclusively that the alpha particle is the nucleus of the helium atom. We begin the study by determining the charge carried by a known number of alpha particles. This is done by allowing the particles to fall on a plate connected to an electrometer and measuring the total charge received by the plate. Dividing this charge by the total number of particles involved, we obtain the charge of a single alpha particle. This was found to be 3.19×10^{-19} coulomb, or just about twice the charge on an electron, but opposite in sign—that is positive, where the electron is negative. From this value and the knowledge of the charge-mass ratio, we can calculate the mass of the alpha particle as 6.62×10^{-24} gm. This is four times the mass of the hydrogen atom which has a mass of 1.67×10^{-24} gm.

Since helium has an atomic weight of 4 and an atomic number of 2, the speculation arose that the alpha particle might be the nucleus of a helium atom. In 1909, Rutherford and a colleague named Royds made the identification certain by subjecting to spectroscopic analysis the alpha particles emitted by a radioactive element called radon. In their test, they collected the particles into a spectroscopic tube which had been thoroughly emptied of air. After gathering alpha particles for about six days through a thin window in the tube, they had accumulated enough particles to produce an electrical discharge through the tube by application of a high voltage. With a spectroscope, they examined the light released by this discharge and observed the spectrum of helium. This evidence clinched the case: by capturing electrons in passing through the walls of the glass tube, the alpha particles become helium atoms.

VELOCITIES OF ALPHA PARTICLES

The speed with which an alpha particle travels when it is emitted by a radioactive element is one of its most important properties. This speed can be measured by making the particle move at right angles to an intense magnetic field and ascertaining

Velocities of Alpha Particles from Some Isotopes

Z	Element	A	Radioactive Isotope	Velocity in 10^9 cm/sec
83	Bismuth	214	Radium C	1.628
				1.619
		212	Thorium C	1.711
				1.705
				1.665
				1.645
				1.642
84	Polonium	210	Polonium	1.597
		215	Actinium A	1.882
		218	Radium A	1.699
86	Emanation	222	Radon	1.625
88	Radium	226	Radium	1.517
				1.488

the radius of its circular path. Alpha particles move at approximately 10,000 miles per second (1.6×10^9 cm/sec). This is a comparatively high speed for such massive particles, but much more interesting is the fact that it is characteristic of the isotope which ejected the particle (see the table on page 142).

In some cases, as in radon, an isotope of the element called emanation—$Z = 86$, $A = 222$—all the alpha particles emitted have the same speed. In other instances, such as radium—$A = 226$—the alpha particles are emitted with one of two speeds. In a few cases, such as thorium C, a radioactive isotope of bismuth—$A = 212$—there are several speeds characteristic of the emitted alpha particles. As a matter of record, the characteristic speed of an alpha particle has been used to ascertain the nature of the isotope releasing it. We shall return to a consideration of these speeds later in our study of the structure of the nucleus.

SCATTERING OF ALPHA PARTICLES BY NUCLEI

The alpha particle, which is relatively massive, possesses a substantial quantity of kinetic energy. Its mass is about 7,500 times greater than an electron's and its kinetic energy is at least several million electron volts. It therefore forms an ideal projectile for use in exploring some of the properties of other atoms. Beginning about 1910, Rutherford and his co-workers, Geiger and Marsden, initiated a series of experiments in which they fired alpha particles of specific energy at thin metallic foils (Figure 5). Most of the particles pierced the foil without deviating. Many

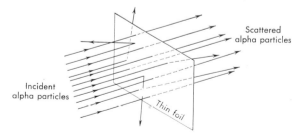

Figure 5   Alpha particles directed against a thin foil. Most of them go through the foil either without any deviation or with very slight deviations from the original direction. A few alpha particles, however, are deviated through very large angles.

others were deviated or scattered through small angles. But a few were deviated through angles greater than 90°; these were scattered backward, that is, toward the side of the foil facing the oncoming beam.

As we noted, alpha particles carry a positive charge about twice that of an electron. Because of their tremendous energy and great mass, the only way for the experimenters to account for the reverse scattering was to assume that the particles came very close to another massive, charged particle. Moreover, since most of the alpha particles went through the foil with little or no deviation, the massive, charged particles must have been tiny in size compared with the distance between them (Figure 6), the scientists reasoned.

On the basis of these experiments, Rutherford, in 1911, proposed his nuclear theory of the atom. The studies were then extended to determine the nuclear charge and the nuclear radius as well as to induce nuclear disintegrations artificially by bombarding the nuclei with alpha particles. The outcome of many different types of experiments showed that the radius R of a nucleus of an atom of mass number A is expressed approximately by the equation

$$R = 1.4 \times 10^{-13} A^{1/3} \text{ cm}.$$

Since A does not exceed 260 for any atom, in all probability, the values of R range from one to less than seven times 1.4×10^{-13} cm. We may remember that x-ray data indicated the distance between atomic centers in crystals was 10^{-8} cm, or 10,000 to 100,000 times the sizes of the nuclei; from this it should become apparent that even in a solid the nuclei are spread comparatively far apart.

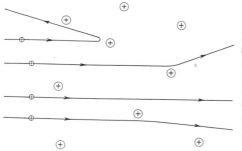

Figure 6   Schematic diagram showing the paths of some alpha particles through a thin foil. The distances between nuclei (larger circles) are much greater than those shown here. A close approach of an alpha particle to a nucleus will therefore be a very rare event.

RADIOACTIVE DISINTEGRATION BY ALPHA-PARTICLE EMISSION

The nucleons inside the nucleus of an isotope have large amounts of energy resulting from the actions of the electrical and the specifically nuclear forces. To explain the emission of an alpha particle from a nucleus containing A nucleons—that is, N neutrons and Z protons—we must imagine a situation in which two protons and two neutrons form a single unit, an alpha particle, and then acquire enough kinetic energy to be able to escape from the nucleus. Generally speaking, this is a rare event. For any specific nucleus, say a radium nucleus, it is impossible in terms of our present state of knowledge to predict when such an event may occur. A nucleus may disintegrate immediately, or within the next second, or it may remain a radium nucleus for a billion years. Yet if we begin with a large number of these nuclei, we find a constant rate of disintegration. This rate can be expressed in terms of the *half-life* of the isotope; by definition, this is *the time required for a given mass of an isotope to disintegrate to half its original value.* For radium—$A = 226$—the half-life is 1,620 years.

Energy released by radioactive disintegration stems from the masses of the particles concerned. For example, when radium—$Z = 88$ and $A = 226$—emits an alpha particle, the product is an atom of the element emanation; this particular isotope is known as radium emanation, or radon—$Z = 86$, $A = 226$. This disintegration may be expressed in the following nuclear reaction equation:

$$_{88}Ra^{226} \rightarrow {}_{86}Rn^{222} + {}_2He^4 + Q.$$

In this equation $_2He^4$ represents the alpha particle and Q the energy liberated in the disintegration process. The lower left-hand number is the atomic number and the upper right-hand number, the mass number of the isotope. The value of Q may be obtained from the known atomic masses of the particles involved. It works out to 4.88 Mev. That is

mass of Ra	= 226.10309	amu,
mass of Rn	= 222.09397	amu,
mass of He	= 4.00388	amu,
mass of final products	= 226.09785	amu,
mass difference = Q	= 0.00524	amu.

Since 1 amu = 931 Mev, the disintegration energy Q can be expressed as $Q = 4.88$ Mev.

The kinetic energy of the alpha particle emitted by radium, measured from its velocity, is 4.80 Mev. The difference between the two values results from the recoil of the product nucleus that occurs when an alpha particle is ejected. Although the momentum of the particle is equal and opposite to the momentum of the new nucleus, the latter's velocity and kinetic energy are much smaller.

DISINTEGRATION BY BETA-PARTICLE EMISSION

When a radioactive isotope disintegrates through the emission of a beta particle—that is, an electron—the atomic number of the resultant nucleus increases by one, while the mass number remains unchanged. This means that the neutron number must decrease by one since $A = Z + N$. Suppose the radioactive isotope of bismuth—$Z = 83$, $A = 210$—emits a beta particle; the product nucleus of the isotope, also known sometimes as radium E, would be polonium—$Z = 84$, $A = 210$. We may write this radioactive disintegration which, incidentally, has a half-life of five days, as the following nuclear reaction equation:

$$_{83}\mathrm{Bi}^{210} \rightarrow {}_{84}\mathrm{Po}^{210} + \beta + Q,$$

in which Q, the energy released in the reaction, comes from the difference in masses of original and final particles. On the basis of the foregoing information we should expect to find that the beta particles emitted by the bismuth isotope all have the same velocity. This is not the case. When these velocities are measured by a magnetic spectrograph, a continuous distribution of velocities is noted, until a maximum velocity is reached; in other words, there is a continuous distribution of energies among the beta particles. This distribution of energies is called an *energy spectrum*.

Figure 7 depicts this spectrum for the beta particles released by Bi^{210}. Its vertical axis pertains to the number of beta particles within a given range of energy; its horizontal axis concerns the energy of these particles expressed in Mev. There is a continuous distribution of energy, it may be seen, up to the maximum value, or *end-point energy*.

To support these facts about radioactive disintegration by

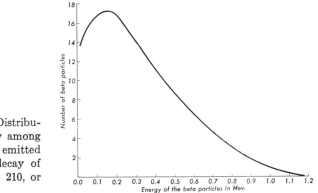

Figure 7 Distribution of energy among beta particles emitted in the beta decay of bismuth, $A = 210$, or radium E.

beta-particle emission, also known as *beta decay*, we might imagine a neutron in the nucleus to split into a proton and an electron with the proton remaining in the nucleus and the electron ejected from it. This would not account, however, for the continuous distribution of energy among the beta particle. It was suggested in 1931 by W. Pauli that this difficulty could be overcome by assuming that two particles are emitted in beta decay, an electron and a new type of particle called a *neutrino*. The neutrino is a neutral particle of negligible mass in comparison with the mass of an electron. In Pauli's assumption, the total energy is shared by the electron and the neutrino. That being the case, the neutrino is emitted with scarcely any energy when the electron is emitted with a large amount, and vice versa.

By its own nature, the neutrino is an elusive particle. Most of the evidence for its actual existence is indirect. But several experiments performed in recent years confirm that it does exist. Our present theory of beta decay, therefore, can be represented by the equation

$$n \text{ (in nucleus)} \rightarrow p \text{ (in nucleus)} + \beta + \nu,$$

with n representing the neutron, p the proton, β the ejected electron, and ν the neutrino.

NATURE AND ORIGIN OF GAMMA RAYS

This leaves the gamma rays. In many cases, as we have pointed out, they accompany the emission of alpha and beta particles in the disintegration process. They may be shown by interference and diffraction experiments to have the same nature as x-rays. The gamma-ray spectrum of any one element is a sharp-line spectrum. Some of the longer gamma-ray wavelengths have been measured with a single-crystal spectrometer, while shorter ones have been studied with a modified type of instrument, a curved spectrometer. Besides, indirect methods have been used widely to determine the energies of gamma rays; these have included the measurements of the energies of electrons ejected in a photoelectric effect with gamma rays, or in a Compton effect (Chapter 9).

Just as x-rays were shown to be emitted as a result of changes in atomic-energy states, so the release of gamma rays can be ascribed to nuclear-energy changes. When any nucleus emits an alpha or beta particle, the new nucleus formed—the *product nucleus*—may be left in a state of higher energy. It could achieve a normal state by releasing gamma rays of suitable energy. One example can illustrate the point (Figure 8).

When radium emits an alpha particle, the product nucleus is the nucleus of the isotope radon. A gamma ray of wavelength $\lambda = 0.0652$A accompanies the action. The energy of this gamma-ray photon is 0.19 Mev. It is derived through knowing, as we do,

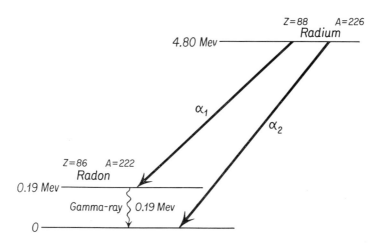

Figure 8   Disintegration of radium by emission of an alpha particle to form radon. If α_1 is emitted, the radon nucleus is formed in an excited state. It then goes to the ground state by emitting a gamma-ray photon.

that the alpha particles of radium have two slightly different velocities, and, therefore, two slightly different energies. The difference between these energies, 0.19 Mev, is the energy of the gamma-ray photon. Put another way, when a normal radium nucleus loses a higher-energy alpha particle, the radon nucleus is in its normal state; but when a lower-energy particle is emitted, the radon nucleus, left in a state of higher energy, needs to emit a gamma-ray photon of appropriate energy—in this case, 0.19 Mev—to reach the normal or ground state.

12 RADIOACTIVE DECAY

THE LIFETIME OF AN ATOM

In a study of radioactivity one question that comes to mind at once concerns the lifetime of an atom. What is an atom's lifetime; how long does it last? The term *lifetime* is both apt and appropriate because in the disintegration of an atom by particle emission, the original atom vanishes and is replaced by a newly produced successor. The original may be called the *parent atom* and its successor, the *daughter atom*. Exactly when the original will expire and the new atom take its place is unpredictable; the disintegration of any one atom may occur within the next second, or not for another billion years.

But we can get some idea of the average lifetime of an atom by applying a statistical approach and following the same principles used to forecast the average lifespan of an individual human. Among any large group of identical atoms, the number that will disintegrate in any specified interval of time depends directly on the size of the group. The larger the number of atoms involved, the greater will be the number that disintegrate in the next short time-span. The rate of this decay can be measured by counting the number of alpha particles, or beta particles, emitted in a fixed time-period. From this, the average lifetime of any one atom can be found by multiplying the number of disintegrating atoms by the time each of them existed, then adding these products for all the atoms involved, and finally dividing this sum by the total number of atoms.

Figure 1 represents graphically the results of measuring the decay of a given radioactive isotope. By starting at a time

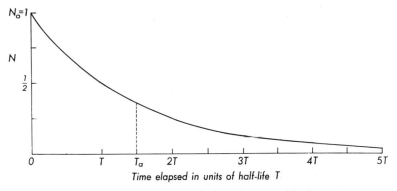

Figure 1   Decay of radioactive element with time.

called zero with a number of atoms N_0 of the isotope, the number of atoms remaining active at a later time will be less than N_0. After a certain time lapse T, half of the original atoms will have disintegrated. This time interval T is the half-life of the isotope. During this period, the activity of the isotope also will have fallen to half its original value. The same phenomenon recurs in a second interval T; the remaining number of atoms will again drop by one-half so that at the end of this span, only a fourth of the original atoms survive.

In the graph, the scale of time is plotted along the horizontal axis with the half-life T as the unit of time. The graph is an *exponential curve* that approaches the horizontal—or time—axis, but never actually reaches it. The relationship between the half-life of a radioactive isotope and the average lifetime T_a, therefore, can be shown to be represented by the equation

$$T = 0.693 \, T_a,$$

which is the value depicted in Figure 1. It follows that by obtaining the half-life of any radioactive isotope, we may determine its average lifetime with ease.

The half-lives, and hence the average lifetimes, vary widely among the naturally radioactive isotopes. Radium, for example, has a half-life of 1,620 years, while its daughter, radon—or radium emanation—has a half-life of 3.82 days. Some isotopes have very brief lifespans measured in millionths of a second, others have lifetimes of billions of years.

If we start now with a milligram of radon, there will be
only ½ milligram left in 3.82 days and the number of alpha
particles emitted per second will also have decreased by half. At
the end of 7.64 days—2T—only ¼ milligram will survive; at the
end of 19.1 days—5T—¹⁄₃₂ milligram of the radon will be left and
its activity will have diminished to one thirty-second of its
original quantity.

PROBABILITY OF DECAY

The rate at which any radioactive isotope decays is constant,
irrespective of the isotope's physical and chemical conditions.
The decaying process is unaffected by such things as temperature,
pressure, and whether the isotope is a solid, liquid, or gas; similarly, the fact that the isotope may be in isolation or in chemical
combination with other elements has no bearing on decay. But
decay may be detected anywhere by its radioactivity.

Although we cannot predict exactly when any atom will
disintegrate, we can assess the *probability of its decay*. The
longer the average lifetime of an atom the smaller will be its
probability of decay. This can be expressed by the following
formula in which λ represents the probability of decay:

$$\lambda = 1/T_a.$$

The Greek letter λ is known also as the disintegration constant
of the particular radioactive isotope. It symbolizes the fractional
decrease of the isotope in a specified unit of time. Any successful
theory of nuclear structure must be able to account for the
process of radioactive decay. One test for checking the validity
of a theory is whether it can predict successfully the decay rate
of any particlar isotope.

RADIOACTIVE SERIES

Most of the natural radioactive isotopes are genetically related and fit into one of three radioactive series. Each series
begins with a long-lived parent and ends with a stable isotope
of lead. The three series are the uranium, the thorium, and the
actinium. The uranium series starts with the uranium isotope
$Z = 92$ and $A = 238$, and has a half-life of 4.5 billion years. The

thorium series starts with thorium, $Z = 90$, $A = 232$, and has as its half-life 13.9 billion years. The actinium series begins with actino-uranium, actually an isotope of uranium, $Z = 92$, $A = 235$, and has a half-life of 880 million years.

Figure 2 shows the genetic relationships for the uranium series. In the earlier days of the study of radioactivity, each radioactive isotope was given a special name and symbol. Nowadays the isotopes are identified simply by the chemical name

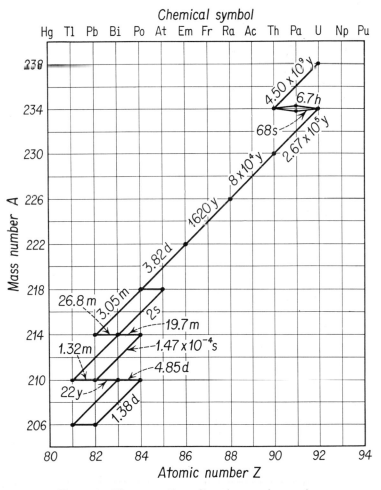

Figure 2　The naturally radioactive uranium series.

of the element and the appropriate mass number A for the concrete atomic number Z.

In the illustration (Figure 2), the chemical symbol for the element is at the top of the horizontal axis and the atomic number at the bottom. The mass number is plotted on the vertical axis. Since an alpha particle is the nucleus of an atom of helium —$Z = 2$, $A = 4$—emission of the particle produces a new atom with an atomic number two less than that of the parent atom and a mass number four less than its parent's. The emission of a beta particle does not affect the mass number of the nucleus but does precipitate an increase of the atomic number by one. In addition, the emission of a negative beta particle is accompanied by the change of a neutron into a proton in the new nucleus.

The last isotope that terminates this uranium series is lead, $Z = 82$, $A = 206$. The terminal isotope of the thorium series is also lead, $Z = 82$, $A = 208$. For the actinium series, the ultimate isotope, lead, is $Z = 82$, $A = 207$. Although these particular isotopes are stable—that is, they lack radioactivity—other isotopes of lead are radioactive. In the graphic representation (Figure 2), you will note the half-lives of all the radioactive isotopes of the uranium series expressed in terms of years, days, hours, minutes, or seconds.

AGE OF THE EARTH

Uranium is dispersed widely over the surface of the earth. Every ore bearing uranium contains not only uranium but also all the products of disintegration in its genetic series. By knowing the lifetimes of the various isotopes in the uranium series, it becomes possible to calculate how much of a particular product will be formed in a specific period of time from one or more grams of uranium. If we assume that at the time of the solidification of the earth's crust the particular isotope of lead in the uranium series did not exist, then a measurement of the *ratio of this lead to the amount of uranium present* will provide the age of the rock or mineral containing it. One other assumption implied is that the quantity of each isotope in the uranium chain, from uranium to lead, has not been affected by physical or chemical processes in all this time. This explains the need for a wide sampling of uranium-bearing ores and minerals throughout the world to establish the age of the earth.

The age of mineral obtained from the uranium-lead ratio sets a lower limit to the age of the earth—that is, the earth is older than the mineral. By this method, the age of the earth is found to be about three billion years. Similar results have been obtained from the thorium-lead ratio and from other measurements of radioactive isotopes found in the earth's crust. Substantially, they all give the same age for the earth.

ALTERNATE MODES OF DECAY

In most cases, the atoms of any individual radioactive isotope always emit the same kind of particle when they decay (Figure 2). Uranium always emits an alpha particle and thorium a beta particle, for example. But there are other cases such as that of polonium, $A = 218$, in which some atoms decay by alpha-particle emission to form lead, while other atoms decay by beta-particle emission to form another isotope, astatine. In this particular instance, 99.96 per cent of the decay is by alpha-particle emission. The daughter atoms then decay by different modes and at different rates to form the same product, bismuth; astatine decays by alpha-particle emission with a half-life of two seconds, while lead disintegrates by beta-particle emission with a half-life of 26.8 minutes. This phenomenon of two alternate modes of decay is sometimes called *branching*.

Branching also takes place in the disintegration of bismuth, $A = 214$. Here the predominant mode is beta-particle emission. The daughters once more decay at different rates to form the same product, a radioactive isotope of lead, $Z = 82$, $A = 210$. The branching phenomenon is also quite common in the other radioactive series.

NUCLEAR ISOMERS

One observation worth noting in the decay of thorium is that the daughter, protactinium—$Z = 91$, $A = 234$—disintegrates by beta-particle emission with two different half-lives, one of 68 seconds and the other of 6.7 hours. At one time, it was assumed that a particular half-life applied only to one specific

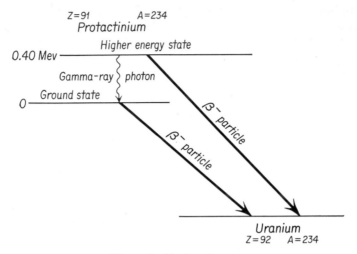

Figure 3   Nuclear isomers.

isotope and that apparently two different isotopes were formed on occasions in the same type of decay. These two types of nuclei, shown in Figure 2 by a slight separation of points which should actually coincide, were given different names. In 1921, however, experiments undertaken by Hahn found that only one isotope formed in the beta-decay of thorium but that the nuclei could be in two different energy states.

Figure 3 contains the two energy states of protactinium. The higher one contains about 0.4 Mev more energy than the lower, or *ground state*. Most of the atoms in the higher energy state disintegrate by beta-particle emission with a half-life of 68 seconds. These form uranium, $A = 234$. A small portion of the nuclei in the higher energy state, however, first go to the ground state by emitting a gamma-ray photon of 0.4 Mev and the nuclei thus formed decay by beta-particle emission with a half-life of 6.7 hours to produce uranium $A = 234$.

Nuclei in different energy states that last long enough to be measured are called *nuclear isomers*, and the energy states are called *isomeric states*. For many years, the foregoing example of nuclear isomerism was unique. But with the discovery of artificial radioactivity, the number of isomeric nuclei has grown enormously.

13 DISINTEGRATION OF NUCLEI

Nuclei are much too small to be seen even with the most powerful microscopes. Yet individual nuclear events can be made visible. In passing through a substance, for instance, charged particles ionize some of the substance's atoms and molecules, and these ions in many cases can be made to produce visible effects.

The assisting agent in this process is the photographic plate which has been used in nuclear studies since Becquerel discovered radioactivity. These photographic plates are covered with emulsions containing silver bromide. When the charged particles go through the emulsion, the action separates the silver bromide into silver and bromine. In the eventual developing of the plate, the bromine is removed leaving only the silver. The length of the tracks created by the particle in the emulsion is minute. Therefore, the plates must be examined under a microscope to make the tracks visible.

Photographic plates used in nuclear physics have thick emulsions, from approximately 0.02 mm to 2.0 mm in depth. These emulsions contain much greater concentrations of silver bromide than ordinary emulsions. Their sensitivity to different types of charged particles, moreover, can be controlled.

Another tracking device is the Wilson cloud chamber designed and developed by C. T. R. Wilson (Figure 1). It consists of a cylindrical chamber C containing a gas saturated with water vapor. The chamber is illuminated by light from a strong source that enters through a window. The tracks may be viewed or photographed through the glass cover. These are produced

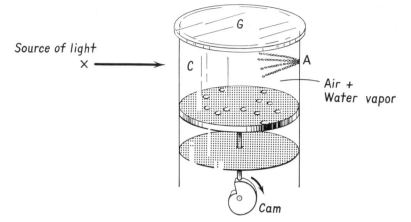

Figure 1   A Wilson cloud-chamber.

when a movable piston P is lowered suddenly, causing the gas in the chamber, which is air, to expand. The sudden expansion precipitates a drop in the temperature of the air so that the air becomes supersaturated with water vapor. Some of this water vapor will condense on any charged particle in its vicinity, forming a liquid droplet. If an alpha particle moves through the air, for example, it will produce from 20,000 to 50,000 ion pairs for every centimeter of its path. If the air is expanded suddenly, the supersaturated water vapor condenses on these ions and forms a visible track. The length of this track, or the *range* of the alpha particle in the air, depends on the particle's energy.

Figure 2   Tracks of alpha particles from a combination of Bi 214 and Po 214 in a Wilson cloud-chamber showing two distinct ranges. (*From J. Rutherford, J. Chadwick, and C. D. Ellis*, Radiations from Radioactive Substances. *By permission of The Macmillan Company, publishers.*)

Figure 2 contains a photograph of the tracks of alpha particles emitted by radioactive substances, in this case, a combination of bismuth 214 and polonium 214. Note the two distinct ranges for these tracks. The tracks are essentially straight almost to the end of the range. Any departure from the straight line indicates an encounter between an alpha particle and some nucleus in the air of the chamber.

NUCLEAR DISINTEGRATION BY ALPHA-PARTICLE BOMBARDMENT

The artificial transmutation of one element into another was accomplished for the first time by Rutherford in 1919. A diagram of the apparatus he used in a simple type of experiment appears in Figure 4. In the experiment, the chamber C was filled with a gas—nitrogen—and alpha particles from a radioactive source A were absorbed in the nitrogen. A sheet of silver foil F, thick enough to absorb the alpha particles, was placed over an opening in the side of the chamber. Outside the opening, Rutherford placed a zinc sulphide screen S and a microscope M for observing any scintillations produced on the screen. He concluded from finding scintillations when the chamber was filled with nitrogen that they were produced by high-energy particles ejected by nuclei of the nitrogen under bombardment by the alpha particles. Experiments in magnetic deflection disclosed that the high-

Figure 3 Ernest Rutherford (1871–1937). He discovered properties of alpha and beta rays. Originated the nuclear theory of the structure of the atom. Performed the first successful experiments on the artificial disintegration of nuclei. (*Courtesy of Ramsey & Muspratt, Cambridge, England.*)

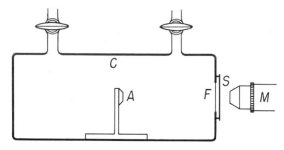

Figure 4   Diagram of the apparatus used by Rutherford in the first successful experiments on artificial disintegration of atomic nuclei.

energy particles were protons, or hydrogen nuclei. In addition, other light elements—in the range from boron to potassium—were also disintegrated by bombardment with alpha particles.

The disintegration of nuclei in this way has also been studied with the Wilson cloud chamber. Here again the chamber is filled with nitrogen whose nuclei are to be bombarded, and a source of alpha particles is placed at one end of the chamber. Figure 5 shows a series of alpha particle tracks in a cloud chamber filled with nitrogen. Most of these tracks are straight, but one of them branches out in two directions after traveling a

Figure 5   A pair of steroscopic photographs of alpha-particle tracks showing a collision with a nitrogen nucleus which results in the ejection of a proton. (*From J. Rutherford, J. Chadwick, and C. D. Ellis,* Radiations from Radioactive Substances. *By permission of The Macmillan Company, publishers.*)

short distance in the gas. The longer, thinner track is produced by a proton. The shorter, thicker one is produced by a more massive particle, identified as oxygen.

THE COMPOUND NUCLEUS

In 1936, Bohr advanced a theory of the nucleus that suggests that the disintegration of nitrogen by bombardment with alpha particles may be considered to consist of two parts. The first of these is the *capture* of the alpha particle by the nitrogen nucleus, resulting in the formation of a new *compound nucleus*. The second part is the immediate disintegration of the compound nucleus into two particles, one of which is a proton (Figure 6). These two processes are represented in the following *nuclear reaction* equation analogous to one representing a chemical reaction:

$$_2\text{He}^4 + {_7}\text{N}^{14} \rightarrow (_9\text{F}^{18}) \rightarrow {_8}\text{O}^{17} + {_1}\text{H}^1 + Q.$$

Since the total charge must be conserved, the atomic number of the compound nucleus has to be the sum of the atomic numbers of helium and nitrogen. In this case, the compound nucleus is fluorine, $Z = 9$. As this isotope of fluorine disintegrates with the emission of a proton, the remaining part, the product nucleus, must be oxygen, $Z = 8$.

The guiding principle in determining which of an element's isotopes is formed during a nuclear reaction is this: the mass number of the compound nucleus must equal the sum of the mass numbers of the initial particles as well as the sum of the mass numbers of the final particles. This is not the same as the principle of conservation of mass. Mass may be converted into energy

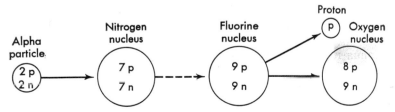

Figure 6 An alpha particle, directed toward a nitrogen nucleus, may penetrate it, forming a compound nucleus of fluorine, which then disintegrates into a fast-moving proton and a nucleus of oxygen.

and energy into mass. In fact, the initial and final masses of the atoms are not equal; the difference between the masses of the initial and final particles is the *nuclear reaction energy*, Q. When the sum of the masses of the final particles is greater than the sum of the masses of the initial particles, energy is absorbed in the reaction from the initial kinetic energies of the particles and Q is negative. But when the sum of the masses of the final particles is less than the sum of the masses of the initial particles, this difference in mass is released in the form of kinetic energy of the final particles and Q now is positive.

In the foregoing nuclear reaction, for example, the masses of the initial and final particles are

$$
\begin{array}{ll}
_2\text{He}^4 = 4.00388 & _8\text{O}^{17} = 17.00453 \\
_7\text{N}^{14} = \underline{14.00755} & _1\text{H}^1 = \underline{1.00815} \\
\phantom{_7\text{N}^{14} =} 18.01143 & \phantom{_1\text{H}^1 =} 18.01268
\end{array}
$$

The masses of the final particles exceed those of the initial particles. Therefore the value of Q is negative and equals -0.00125 amu, which is equivalent to -1.16 Mev. This energy must come from the initial kinetic energy of the alpha particle for the nuclear reaction to occur.

Two typical reactions involving alpha-particle capture and emission of protons—sometimes called a-p reactions—are

$$
_{13}\text{Al}^{27} + \, _2\text{He}^4 \rightarrow (_{15}\text{P}^{31}) \rightarrow \, _{14}\text{Si}^{30} + \, _1\text{H}^1
$$
$$
_{19}\text{K}^{39} + \, _2\text{He}^4 \rightarrow (_{21}\text{Sc}^{43}) \rightarrow \, _{20}\text{Ca}^{42} + \, _1\text{H}^1.
$$

The protons emitted in these reactions have definite energy ranges. This is interpreted as showing definite energy levels in the nucleus. The normal state of the product nucleus is achieved by the ejection of protons with maximum energy. When the protons are ejected with less than maximum, the nucleus is left in an excited state, or a state of higher energy, and may only return to the normal state by emission of a gamma-ray photon. Gamma rays of the right amount of energy have been observed in these reactions.

DISCOVERY OF THE NEUTRON

The capture of an alpha particle does not inevitably cause the emission of a proton by the compound nucleus. In one particular reaction resulting from the bombardment of beryllium by alpha particles, a penetrating type of radiation was found to be released by the compound nucleus. Various efforts to explain this fact on the basis of gamma rays led to many discrepancies. Finally, in 1932, J. Chadwick, after numerous experiments, suggested that the radiation consisted of neutral particles, called *neutrons*. These have a mass nearly equal to the mass of protons. The reaction that takes place is

$$_4Be^9 + {_2He^4} \rightarrow (_6C^{13}) \rightarrow {_6C^{12}} + {_0n^1},$$

in which $_0n^1$ represents the neutron, indicating it has zero charge and mass number 1. This type of reaction is called an $a\text{-}n$ reaction.

Figure 7 shows one arrangement used by Chadwick to demonstrate the existence and properties of neutrons. The source of alpha particles is a disk D on which polonium has been deposited. The disk and the beryllium target are placed in an evacuated chamber C. The neutrons emanating from the beryllium pass through the thin wall of the chamber and enter I, an ionization chamber, through the window W. The ionization chamber is connected to an amplifier and then to some recording device such as an electrical counter or loud-speaker.

Because the neutrons have no charge, they do not produce any ionization in their passage through the chamber. But some neutrons which strike the walls of the ionization chamber cause the ejection of nuclei and these then produce ions in the chamber. The ions are recorded in the electrical counter or the loud-speaker. If the recording device is a loud-speaker, a click will be heard every time a nucleus produces intense ionization.

Now when neutrons from beryllium go directly into the chamber, only a few counts per minute will be recorded. This is not affected appreciably by placement of thin sheets of lead in

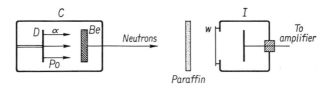

Figure 7   Arrangement of apparatus for the detection of neutrons.

front of the chamber. But the number of counts per minute increases markedly when a thin slab of paraffin is slipped between the chamber C and the ionization chamber I. The increase results from the fact that neutrons, in colliding with the nuclei of the hydrogen atoms contained in the paraffin, give up a large part of their energy to these protons and eject them from the paraffin. The protons enter the ionization chamber where they are recorded by the ionization they themselves produce.

Since discovery of the neutron, many different nuclear reactions have been used to obtain them. From these tests the mass of a neutron has been determined accurately. It is 1.00899. Because they are without charge, the neutrons should be able to penetrate atomic nuclei easily. Moreover, study of the reactions that supply neutrons should provide valuable information about nuclear properties and reactions.

DISCOVERY OF THE POSITRON

Another new particle, the *positron,* was discovered in 1932, the same year as the finding of the neutron. Its discoverer, Carl D. Anderson, came upon it while investigating cosmic-ray phenomena with a Wilson cloud chamber. Cosmic rays consist of a wide variety of radiations which continually traverse the atmosphere of the earth. The exact nature and origin of the *primary* cosmic rays are unknown, but from studies of other cosmic rays at various depths below the top of the atmosphere, several new particles and new types of nuclear reactions have been detected. (Chapter 17.)

In Anderson's experiment, the Wilson cloud chamber was placed in a magnetic field. Expansions of the chamber occurred at definite intervals and photographs were taken of the tracks formed during the expansions. In one photograph, a track was noted as having the same appearance as that of an electron, but with a curvature opposite to that of an electron with a negative charge. To make identification certain, Anderson placed a lead plate 6 mm thick in the center of the chamber and photographed it (Figure 8). The particle lost some of its energy in passing through the lead plate. The curvature of its path above the plate was found to be greater than below it and therefore the particle must have originated at the bottom of the chamber. From known

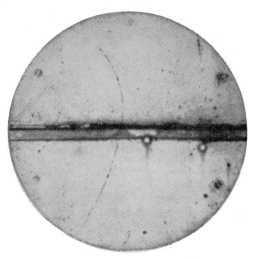

Figure 8 Cloud-chamber photograph of the path of a positron in a magnetic field. The positron originated at the bottom of the chamber and passed through a sheet of lead 6 mm. thick. (*Photograph by Carl D. Anderson.*)

directions of both the magnetic field and the curvature of the path, it was concluded that the particle had to be positively charged. This particle was given the name *positron*; measurements show it has the same mass as an electron and the same charge, but that its sign is opposite. The symbol frequently used to represent it is $_{+1}e^0$; it is also called sometimes a β^+ particle.

Shortly after Anderson's discoverey, sources of positrons were found among many of the artificially produced radioactive substances.

ARTIFICIAL OR INDUCED RADIOACTIVITY

While bombarding the nuclei of some of the lighter elements with alpha particles, Frederic and Irene Joliot-Curie, son-in-law and daughter of the famous Curies, observed that the bombarded substances continued to emit radiations even after the source of alpha particles had been removed. Ionization measurements and experiments utilizing magnetic deflection demonstrated that the radiations consisted of positrons. In addition, the intensity of the radiation was found to decrease with time just as radiations from a naturally radioactive substance. The half-life of the positron radiation was measured in each case; this was the first time that radioactivity was ever induced in a substance.

One of the reactions was the bombardment of boron by

alpha particles accompanied by the emission of neutrons. This was the reaction equation

$$_5B^{10} + {_2}He^4 \rightarrow (_7N^{14}) \rightarrow {_7}N^{13} + {_0}n^1.$$

Now, nitrogen of mass number 13 is not a stable isotope. It disintegrates with the emission of a positron. And this is the appropriate equation

$$_7N^{13} \rightarrow {_6}C^{13} + {_{+1}}e^0$$

with half-life $T = 10$ min. The symbol $_{+1}e^0$ represents the positron; its charge is equal to a proton's and its mass number is zero. The carbon atom of mass number 13 is a stable isotope of carbon.

The identification of the radioactive atom as nitrogen was made certain by chemical analysis. Special methods for analysis have to be developed in each case as the amount available for this purpose is minute. For example, in the boron reaction, the target was made of boron nitride. After being bombarded with alpha particles for several minutes, the target was heated with caustic soda. One of the products of this chemical reaction was gaseous ammonia NH_3. This was found to be radioactive with a half-life of 10 min, showing that the nitrogen of ammonia was the radioactive element.

Since discovery of artificially induced radioactivity, it has become possible to induce radioactivity in all elements by producing at least one radioactive isotope for every element known. It has become possible also to develop new elements, both to fill up the gaps in the periodic table and to extend the number of elements beyond 100. These developments were made possible by two essentially different type of devices—*particle accelerators* and *nuclear reactors*.

RADIOACTIVE DISINTEGRATION BY POSITRON EMISSION

In the study of the naturally radioactive isotopes, we found no cases of positron emission. Among artificially produced radioactive isotopes, positron emission is quite common. Some similarities exist between radioactive decay by electron emission and positron emission. In each instance, the mass numbers of the parent atom and the product atom are the same. The energy spectrum of the positrons from any one isotope has a continuous distribution to a maximum, the end-point energy, similar to an electron's energy spectrum.

Thus we may postulate an analogous process for positron decay: that a proton in the nucleus disintegrates into a neutron, which remains in the nucleus, and a positron and a neutrino, which are ejected from the nucleus. We may write this process as follows:

$$p \text{ (in nucleus)} \rightarrow n \text{ (in nucleus)} + \beta^+ + \nu.$$

There is one important difference between positron β^+ emission and electron β^- emission: the mass of the proton is less than the mass of the neutron. For the above process to occur, the proton needs to acquire sufficient energy from the other nuclear particles to be able to disintegrate into a neutron, positron, and neutrino. The minimum quantity of energy that will suffice is $2m_0c^2$ in which m_0 is the rest mass of the electron (or positron). This may be inferred from the fact that when a positron is emitted by a nucleus of atomic number Z, the atomic number of the product nucleus is $Z - 1$; hence, one of the outer electrons is excessive for this type of atom. Essentially, two electrons are emitted in positron decay, the β^+ from the nucleus and the β^- from the surrounding electrons.

The energy for beta decay comes from the difference in mass between the parent and daughter atoms. For β^+ decay, this difference must be at least $2m_0$. In general, the mass difference is larger, with the remaining amount appearing as kinetic energy of the positron and neutrino.

14 ACCELERATED ATOM SMASHING

ACCELERATING PROGRESS IN SMASHING ATOMS

In the early thirties, physicists throughout the world began to accept the idea that ordinary stable atoms could be disintegrated by bombardment with high energy particles. But to the keen disappointment of many, the opportunities for pursuing the hypothesis were sharply limited by the small supply of the precious radioactive isotopes then known. For example, the entire world had only a few grams of radium available. And the energies of the projectiles such as the alpha particles, beta particles, and gamma-ray photons were confined to a few million electron volts. What the physicists needed were new devices. So they began to design and build machines that could accelerate charged particles to higher energies.

The one way to increase the energy of a charged particle is to subject it to an electrical force. This may be done by applying an electric field to it. The field may be produced by a voltage —a difference of potential—maintained between two points, or by the timed variation of a magnetic field in the region of the charged particle. The betatron is based on the second method. A static magnetic field has little value in this process because it does not contribute to the energy of a charged particle.

It would serve little practical purpose to examine the designs of the many particle accelerators, or "atom smashers," that have been developed in these past years, but we get a clear impression of their general principles from the most popular of them all, the *cyclotron*, completed in 1931 by Ernest O. Lawrence and M. S. Livingston. The success achieved with all these pioneering devices inspired efforts to build bigger and better ones. This took tremendous resources and the combined contributions of many groups. They included physicists, engineers, skilled mechanics, large industrial corporations, and institutions and organizations with large supplies of money.

One may justly ask why the expenditure of so much talent, skill, money, and effort on these bigger atom smashers. The physicist's answer is simple: we are seeking to learn as much as possible about the nucleus. The common objective of all physicists is to fathom the forces that hold together the nucleons, to understand the nature of the particles inside the nucleus, and to follow the processes that go on among the nuclear particles. An enormous quantity of new information has been obtained already and about twenty new particles have been discovered. This has increased the complexity of the problem more than it has furthered our understanding of it. With the additional number of brilliant minds applying themselves to nuclear problems, we feel confident that the laws of nuclear physics will be put into a handy and intellectually satisfying form.

THE CYCLOTRON

The cyclotron, as developed by Lawrence and Livingston, consists basically of a short, hollow cylinder divided into two sections, A and B (Figure 1). Each section is usually called a "dee" because of its resemblance to the letter **D**. The dees are placed in air-tight metal compartments and the complete cylinder is put between the poles of a huge electromagnet, these poles ranging in diameter from 30 to 60 inches. The magnetic field is directed at right angles to the base of the cylinder.

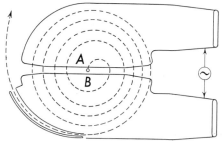

Figure 1   Path of a particle in a cyclotron.

A gas such as hydrogen, helium, or deuterium is pumped into the cylinder and kept at a low pressure. Ions of the gas are produced by bombardment with electrons from a heated filament inside the assembly, or from a separate source that feeds the ions into an opening in the cylinder's walls. The dees are connected to the terminals of a high frequency alternating current that changes the charge on each of them several million times a second.

When A is positive and B is negative any positive ions between them are accelerated toward B. When the ion arrives inside of B, the magnetic field propels it into a circular path. The strength of the field is regulated to permit the ion to complete a semicircle in an interval during which the voltage changes and makes B positive and A negative. The ion now receives an added acceleration as it recrosses the gap, moving this time from B to A. Inside A, it will move with a higher speed even though the radius of the circular path will also be larger. It thus takes the same time to complete a semicircular loop in A and reach the edge of the gap at the right instant to receive another acceleration toward B. The ion will continue to travel in semicircles of increasing radii each time it moves from A to B and from B to A, acquiring additional energy during each passage from one dee to the other.

After the ions traverse many semicircular paths and near the circumference of the cylinder, an auxiliary electric field deflects them out of a window of the chamber. These high energy ions may now be used to bombard the nuclei of substances placed close to the window. Suitable apparatus enables us to study the products of this bombardment.

If hydrogen is the gas in the cyclotron, the high energy particles turn out to be protons. When deuterium is used, the high energy particles are deuterons, but when helium is pumped into the chamber, we obtain an artificial source of high energy alpha particles. The energies of these several kinds of particles range up to ten million electron volts.

There is a practical limit to the amount of energy that can be imparted to the particles in the foregoing type of constant-frequency cyclotron. This is so because the mass of the particle grows with increasing velocity—that is, because of the relativistic effect. As a result, the ions fall out of step with the frequency of the alternating current applied to the dees. This limitation is obviated by the *frequency-modulated cyclotron* also known as the *synchrocyclotron.* For successful operation, this type of atom smasher depends on a property known as *phase stability,* a property discovered independently in 1945 by V. Veksler in the U. S. S. R. and by E. M. McMillan in the United States. Phase stability is possessed by charged particles that move in a combination of a one-directional magnetic field and an alternating electric field of changing frequencies.

Since the mass of a particle increases with each addition of velocity, some of the energy supplied to the particle will enlarge its mass and only a fraction will help to increase its kinetic energy. Such a particle would fall behind if dependent on the applied voltage. But Veksler and McMillan both proved that the particle could receive additional energy by reducing the frequency of the applied voltage or strengthening the magnetic field. In the frequency-modulated cyclotron (Figure 2), the magnetic field

Figure 2   The 184-in. Berkeley cyclotron in operation at the Radiation Laboratory of the University of California at Berkeley. The vacuum chamber is in place between the pole pieces of the electromagnet. The tube extending into the chamber at the left carries the target, which is bombarded by the high-energy ions in the cyclotron chamber. (*Photograph supplied by Professor R. I. Thornton, Radiation Laboratory, University of California, Berkeley, Calif.*)

remains constant while the frequency of the voltage is decreased slowly.

This type of cyclotron has made it possible to produce protons of nearly a half-billion electron volts of energy. Some frequency-modulated cyclotrons have accelerated beryllium nuclei Be^{++++} and carbon nuclei C^{++++++} to energies approaching one billion volts, abbreviated 1 Bev.

Specially designed *proton synchrotrons* such as the Cosmotron at the Brookhaven National Laboratory can accelerate protons to 3 Bev, while the Bevatron at the University of California at Berkeley can accelerate protons to 6 Bev. One atom smasher of this kind in the Soviet Union can accelerate protons to 10 Bev. Other pending machines are expected to accelerate particles to 100 Bev. Each newly achieved range of energy has led to the discovery of new particles and new nuclear phenomena.

DISINTEGRATIONS WITH PROTONS AS PROJECTILES

Many different types of nuclear reactions may be obtained with the high energy protons available at the present time. As one of these protons approaches the nucleus of an atom, it is repelled by the positive charge Ze of the nucleus of atomic number Z. To overcome the repulsion and penetrate the nucleus, the proton needs a sufficient amount of kinetic energy. Once it gets inside the nucleus, the proton becomes subject to the *specifically nuclear forces* whose precise nature is still unknown. The one thing that is known about these forces is that they have a small range of action. This range probably does not exceed the size of a nucleus which is less than 10^{-12} cm.

Inside the nucleus, the proton becomes part of a new nucleus of atomic number $Z + 1$. This is also called the *compound nucleus*. For example, if a proton is hurled at lithium, $Z = 3$ and $A = 7$, the resultant compound nucleus will be beryllium, $Z = 4$ and $A = 8$. This isotope of beryllium, $_4Be^8$, is unstable and may disintegrate in several ways. Two of them are shown by the following nuclear reactions:

$$_3Li^7 + {}_1H^1 \rightarrow ({}_4Be^8) \rightarrow {}_2He^4 + {}_2He^4 + Q$$

or $\qquad _3Li^7 + {}_1H^1 \rightarrow ({}_4Be^8) \rightarrow {}_4Be^8 + \text{gamma rays,}$

followed by $\qquad _4Be^8 \rightarrow {}_2He^4 + {}_2He^4 + Q.$

The proton is represented by its chemical symbol, $_1H^1$. In the first of these reactions, the compound nucleus which is designated by the chemical symbol in parenthesis, ($_4Be^8$), disintegrates into two alpha particles, $_2He^4$, each having about 8.5 Mev of kinetic energy. The symbol Q represents the energy released or absorbed in the reaction. It is equal to the differences in the masses of the initial products and the final products. When Q is positive, energy is released; when Q is negative, energy is absorbed. In the foregoing reactions energy is released.

An alternate way for the reaction to proceed is for the compound nucleus to emit a gamma-ray photon and move to a lower energy state from which it disintegrates into two alpha particles of less kinetic energy. The first of these reactions is sometimes designated as a (p, a) reaction, indicating that the bombarding particle is a proton and one of the products is an alpha particle. The second reaction is designated as a (p, γ) reaction, or sometimes as a proton capture.

One interesting (p, a) reaction which forms $_4Be^8$ is the following:

$$_5B^{11} + {_1H^1} \rightarrow ({_6C^{12}}) \rightarrow {_4Be^8} + {_2He^4} + Q$$

followed by $\qquad _4Be^8 \rightarrow {_2He^4} + {_2He^4} + Q.$

In this case boron, $_5B^{11}$, captures a proton to form a nucleus of carbon. Although C^{12} is one of the stable isotopes of carbon, the carbon formed in this reaction is unstable because its mass is greater than the mass of the stable form. It disintegrates by emitting an alpha particle that leaves a residual nucleus of beryllium. The beryllium nucleus has an extremely short lifetime, disintegrating into two alpha particles in less than 10^{-14} second.

Another type of reaction using protons as the bombarding particles is the (p, d) reaction. In this, a deuteron is one of the final particles. The following is an illustration of this kind of reaction:

$$_4Be^9 + {_1H^1} \rightarrow ({_5B^{10}}) \rightarrow {_4Be^8} + {_1H^2} + Q.$$

Although there is a stable isotope of boron of mass number 10, the mass of the compound nucleus formed in this reaction is greater than the mass of stable $_5B^{10}$, and therefore the compound nucleus disintegrates. This can be verified by a simple calculation in terms of atomic mass units.

$$\text{Stable } {}_5B^{10} = 10.016110 \text{ amu}$$

$$\begin{aligned} {}_1H^1 &= 1.008145 \\ {}_4Be^9 &= 9.015030 \\ \hline ({}_5Be^{10}) &= 10.023175 \end{aligned}$$

Thus, the compound nucleus, $({}_5B^{10})$, has a mass that exceeds the mass of stable isotope, ${}_5B^{10}$, by 0.007065 amu, which is the same as 6.6 Mev.

DISINTEGRATIONS WITH DEUTERONS AS PROJECTILES

The deuteron is the simplest nucleus of those with more than one nucleon. It consists of two nucleons: a proton, and a neutron. The neutron has no electric charge; consequently, the force holding these nucleons together cannot be electrical, but must be a specifically nuclear force. Experiments with deuterons should prove of immense value in learning something about the nature of this kind of force.

Many nuclear reactions have been observed in which the bombarding particle has been a deuteron. One of the simplest and most important among these is the bombardment of a target containing deuterium by a deuteron. Targets of this specification have been made by freezing *heavy water* on a surface kept cold by liquid air. Other deuterium targets have been constructed out of compounds in which the ordinary form of hydrogen has been replaced by deuterium.

Two different nuclear reactions have been noted to result from this kind bombardment:

$$_1H^2 + {}_1H^2 \rightarrow ({}_2He^4) \rightarrow {}_1H^3 + {}_1H^1 + Q$$

and
$$_1H^2 + {}_1H^2 \rightarrow ({}_2He^4) \rightarrow {}_2He^3 + {}_0n^1 + Q.$$

The first of these reactions—a (d, p) reaction—has been studied with the aid of a Wilson cloud chamber (page 158). A look at the tracks in the chamber discloses that the particles were hydrogen nuclei of mass numbers 1 and 3. The Q in this reaction has a value of 4.03 Mev. This knowledge helps find the mass of H^3, usually called tritium, since the masses of H^1 and H^2 are already known. The mass of H^3 is 3.016997 amu.

Tritium is an unstable isotope of hydrogen. It is radioactive and decays with a half-life of 12.5 years. It emits a beta particle with a maximum kinetic energy of only 18,000 ev in the following reaction:

$$_1H^3 \rightarrow {_2}He^3 + \beta^-.$$

The alternate reaction employing deuteron as the projectile produces a neutron and is called a (d, n) reaction. This is one of the most readily available sources of neutrons. It has special value because the neutrons emitted in the course of the reaction are just about homogeneous in energy. The yield of neutrons and their energies increases as the energies of the bombarding deuterons are increased. The value of Q, the reaction energy, is 3.18 Mev. By using this value for Q and the given masses of deuterium and the neutron, it becomes possible to calculate the mass of $_2He^3$.

Let us consider just one other example of deuteron used as a projectile. In this illustration, sodium, $_{11}Na^{23}$, serves as the target. These are the reactions that have been observed:

$$_{11}Na^{23} + {_1}H^2 \rightarrow ({_{12}}Mg^{25}) \rightarrow {_{12}}Mg^{24} + {_0}n^1 + Q$$

and $\quad _{11}Na^{23} + {_1}H^2 \rightarrow ({_{12}}Mg^{25}) \rightarrow {_{11}}Na^{24} + {_1}H^1 + Q$

followed by $\quad _{11}Na^{24} \rightarrow {_{12}}Mg^{24} + \beta^-, \quad T = 15.0$ hr.

The compound nucleus of magnesium, $A = 25$, which is formed in this reaction, disintegrates either by the emission of a neutron to become stable magnesium, $A = 24$, or by emission of a proton which leaves a radioactive form of sodium, $A = 24$. The radioactive isotope of sodium decays with the release of a beta particle (Figure 3). Its half-life is 15.0 hrs.

Sodium is one of the constituents of ordinary table salt, NaCl. It takes part in many biological processes. When a small amount of this salt contains the radioactive form of sodium it may be used as a "tracer" in many physiological studies. For example, suppose you drink some salt water which has a minute content of Na^{24}. It is then possible to trace its progress through the body, and particularly through the blood stream, by placing

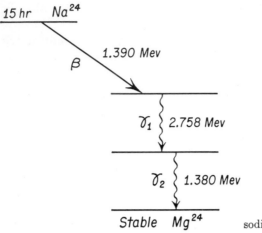

Figure 3   Beta decay of
sodium 24 to magnesium 24.

a Geiger counter near different parts of the body and noting the
beta and gamma rays reaching the counter.

NEUTRONS AS PROJECTILES

As soon as neutrons were discovered, they were put to use
immediately to bombard just about every element in the periodic
table. A neutron's special asset as a projectile is that it can
penetrate a nucleus even if it is moving very slowly. This results
from the fact that a neutron is not repelled by the strong electric
field around the nucleus. One of two things may happen when
a neutron strikes a nucleus of mass number A. Either it may be
captured by the nucleus and form a new nucleus which will be
an isotope of mass number $A + 1$, or it simply may be scattered
or deflected from its original path, giving up some of its energy
to the nucleus in the process. As a rule, the smaller the mass
number of the target nucleus, the greater is the amount of energy
lost by the neutron. If the target is a proton, $A = 1$, the neutron
may give up almost all its energy in a direct collision with the
target nucleus. It was an experiment of this kind which originally
led to discovery of the neutron.

When a slow moving neutron strikes a target containing
protons, such as water or paraffin, it will be captured by a proton
to form a deuteron, as indicated by the following reaction:

$$_1H^1 + _0n^1 \rightarrow (_1H^2) \rightarrow _1H^2 + h\nu.$$

The compound nucleus of deuterium ($_1H^2$) exists in an excited state. It goes to the ground state by emission of a gamma-ray photon, represented by the symbol $h\nu$, in which h is the Planck constant and ν the frequency of the radiation given off as a gamma-ray photon.

The capture of a neutron by a proton is actually the simplest type of nuclear reaction involving specifically nuclear forces. Measurement of the energy released in the form of a gamma-ray photon during the reaction yields the binding energy of these two nucleons. Bell and Elliott obtained a value of 2.23 Mev for the binding energy of a neutron and a proton in a deuteron. For a nuclear process, this is a comparatively small amount of energy; hence, the deuteron may be regarded as a loosely bound entity. The binding energy for nucleons of the heavier nuclei, as we shall see presently, varies from 6 to 8 Mev.

A major nuclear reaction with slow neutrons is the following, involving one of the boron isotopes:

$$_5B^{10} + _0n^1 \rightarrow (_5B^{11}) \rightarrow _3Li^7 + _2He^4 + Q.$$

This (n, a) reaction is used widely as a sensitive detector of the presence of neutrons. A neutron leaves no track of ionized particles in a cloud chamber, photographic emulsion, or other detector because it has no electric charge. But if boron, $A = 10$, is present in the detecting apparatus, the capture of a neutron is signaled by the emission of an alpha particle which can be detected readily. We shall investigate other nuclear processes concerning the capture of neutrons in later chapters, especially the one on fission and fusion.

15 NUCLEAR STRUCTURE

THE PROBLEM OF NUCLEAR STRUCTURE

The wide range of nuclear processes produced since the discovery of artificial disintegration has spawned a vast expansion in the supply of new species of nuclei. More than a thousand varieties are now available. These are tabulated in handbooks of nuclear physics which are kept up to date by government agencies, such as the National Bureau of Standards, and by several of the large university laboratories that engage extensively in the investigation of nuclear species.

The task of digesting this plethora of current data would be made much less arduous by having at hand a suitable model of nuclear structure. But the problem of developing a model of this kind has proved to be much more difficult than the corresponding one for the electronic structure of the atom. Part of the difficulty may be ascribed to the fact that the forces between nucleons are much stronger than the electrical forces between the electrons of the atom, and between the electrons and the nucleus. Several nuclear models have been proposed, but at present there is no single one that is adequate for the broad range of nuclear energies or for the entire range of mass numbers. Each model, however, has a special usefulness for a limited region of energies or a limited range of mass numbers.

What physicists need from a nuclear model is an intellectually acceptable picture of the arrangement of the nucleons in a nucleus, one that can account for the phenomena already known and also serve to predict new phenomena. One problem yearning for solution is the nature of the nuclear force specifically in effect between two nucleons when they are in the nucleus. Another equally important one is whether the physical laws pertaining to extranuclear structure also remain valid for intranuclear structure.

NUCLEAR MODELS

Many nuclear models have been proposed to satisfy this need. Two of them are worth mentioning. The first is the *independent particle model*, or *shell model*, of a nucleus. To develop it, scientists have borrowed as guides several ideas from the electronic shell model of the atom. The major assumption behind this model is that each nucleon moves independently of all its companions in an average nuclear field of force produced by the other nucleons. We shall discuss this in greater detail later on.

The second of the two, the *liquid drop model*, was proposed in 1937 by Niels Bohr. The fundamental assumption on which Bohr's proposal was based is that a nucleus may be considered to behave like a drop of liquid which has a *surface tension* capable of producing forces that lock the nucleons inside. The disintegration of a nucleus by particle emission is similar to the evaporation of molecules from a liquid's surface. It is known that the size of a drop has no bearing on the density of the liquid. This is also true for nuclear matter. Bohr's model proves extremely useful in studying the behavior of compound nuclei and in dealing with *nuclear fission* (Chapter 16).

STABILITY OF NUCLEI

Another approach to the problem of nuclear structure is through statistics. In nature, there are about 250 different isotopes of elements. Most of these isotopes are stable and are grouped into fewer than 100 elements. They may be represented graphically on a neutron-proton diagram (Figure 1), in which the neutron number N of the isotope is plotted against the proton number—or atomic number—Z of the element.

Each point on the graph signifies a stable isotope found in nature. From this, it can be seen that the region of stability is quite narrow. Apart from the very light isotopes, all the points lie above the line for which N and Z are equal, or $N/Z = 1$. More-

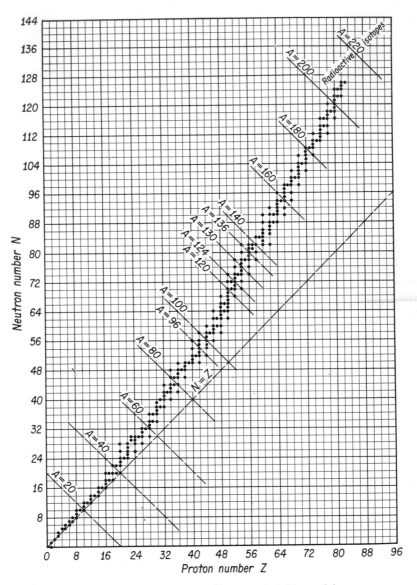

Figure 1   Neutron-proton diagram of stable nuclei.

over, as the higher mass numbers A are plotted, the neutron-proton ratio increases to about 1.6.

A statistical examination of these isotopes indicates that more than half of the stable nuclei contain even numbers of protons and even number of neutrons; these are known as even-even nuclei. About twenty per cent of them have even Z but odd N; they are called even-odd nuclei. An almost equal number of nuclei have odd Z and even N, and are called odd-even nuclei. Only four stable nuclei have odd values for both Z and N. These odd-odd nuclei are $_1H^2$, $_3Li^6$, $_5B^{10}$, and $_7N^{14}$.

PATHS TO NUCLEAR STABILITY

Of the many nuclei known at the present time only some 250 are stable. These lie in the narrow region of stability on the neutron-proton diagram. The others, if represented at all on the diagram, lie to the right or left of this region. These are unstable; they will decay or disintegrate until a stable pattern of nucleons is reached. One of the principal problems of nuclear physics, only partially solved at the moment, is to discover which path a collection of nucleons will follow to reach stability.

Nuclei lying to the left of the stability region on the graph have an excess of neutrons. They may decay by the emission of negative beta particles, during which a neutron is transformed into a proton. In the process, the neutron number is decreased by one and the proton increased by one to leave unchanged the total number of nucleons, or the mass number A. The product, or daughter, nucleus may be stable. If not, another negative beta-decay process may follow to push the nucleus closer to the region of stability. The following chain of beta decays illustrates the point:

$$_{56}Ba^{141} \rightarrow \underset{18\,min}{} _{57}La^{141} \rightarrow \underset{3.7\,hr}{} _{58}Ce^{141} \rightarrow \underset{28\,da}{} _{59}Pr^{141}.$$

The times under the arrows are the half-lives of radioactive decay. The end product is a stable isotope. All these nuclei share the same mass number and are usually called *isobars*.

A competing process with negative beta decay is the emission of the excess neutron. This is a rarer occurrence and generally starts with a highly excited state of the nucleus. For example, krypton, $_{36}Kr^{87}$, may disintegrate to the stable form of $_{36}Kr^{86}$ by the emission of a neutron, or it may decay by two successive

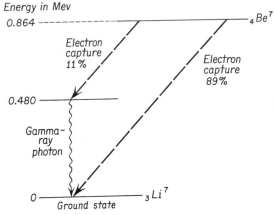

Figure 2   Nuclear decay by electron capture.

negative beta decays to a stable form of strontium, $_{38}Sr^{87}$. Two or more neutrons may be emitted if the nucleus is in a highly excited state.

Nuclei formed with an excess of protons are represented by points lying to the right of the stability region on the neutron-proton diagram. These may decay by the emission of positrons, that is, by positive beta decay, in which case a proton becomes transformed into a neutron. As with negative beta decay, the mass number of the nucleus remains unchanged because the proton number drops by one and the neutron number gains one.

Another method for decreasing the proton number of the nucleus is to capture an electron from the extranuclear part of the atom. This can be the only mode of decay when the difference in energy between the parent and daughter atoms is less than the minimum energy released in positive beta decay. The value of this minimum is $2m_ec^2$, with m_e representing the electronic mass. For example, beryllium, $_4Be^7$, decays to lithium, $_3Li^7$, only by electron capture (Figure 2); the difference in mass between these two atoms is equivalent to 0.875 Mev, while $2m_ec^2$ is equivalent to 1.02 Mev.

Cadmium, $_{48}Cd^{107}$, decays to silver, $_{47}Ag^{107}$, mainly by electron capture and only rarely by positron emission (Figure 3). The nuclear reaction equations for these alternatives are:

electron capture $_{48}Cd^{107} + _{-1}e^0 \rightarrow _{47}Ag^{107}$;

beta decay $_{48}Cd^{107} \rightarrow _{47}Ag^{107} + \beta^+$.

No charged particle is released in the process of electron capture. The captured electron joins the proton to form a neutron and a neutrino, and only the neutrino is emitted. The capture is detected by the x-rays emitted from the product atom. This results from the fact that when an electron moves from the K-shell into the nucleus, the space it vacates will be filled by one of the electrons from an outer shell, with the consequent release of x-rays.

A competing process when there is an excess of protons, particularly when the nucleus is in a highly excited state, is the emission of the excessive proton. This, however, produces a nucleus of a different element than the parent by reducing the atomic number by one. Several reactions of this kind have already been examined.

NUCLEAR SHELL MODEL

It is to be expected that those ideas and concepts which proved so effective in determining the electronic structure of the

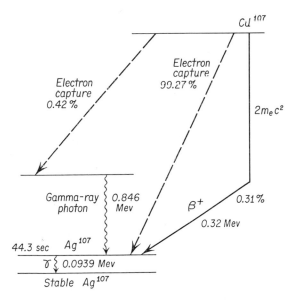

Figure 3   Nuclear decay by either of two processes, positron emission or electron capture.

atom should be carried over into nuclear physics. One of these is the idea of *shell structure* in which certain shells are *closed* to indicate the stability of specific systems which have fixed numbers of nucleons. The concept of closed nuclear shells was advanced first in 1934 by W. Elsasser and again in 1948 by Maria G. Mayer. Present evidence from experiments indicates that closed shells exist for nuclei possessing proton numbers of 2, 8, 20, 28, 50, and 82, and neutron numbers of 2, 8, 20, 28, 50, 82, and 126. These are sometimes called "magic numbers."

Some of the experimental data used in obtaining these magic numbers deals with the number of stable isotopes for a particular element. For example, tin, $Z = 50$, has ten stable isotopes, the largest number of any element. Cadmium, $Z = 20$, has six; nickel, $Z = 28$, has five; oxygen, $Z = 8$, has three. Lead, $Z = 82$, has five stable isotopes; it is also the end product of three naturally radioactive series.

Similar statistical data may be presented for neutrons. For example, there are seven different stable nuclei with N equaling 82. These are $_{54}Xe^{136}$, $_{56}Ba^{138}$, $_{58}Ce^{140}$, $_{59}Pr^{141}$, $_{60}Nd^{142}$, and $_{62}Sm^{144}$. On the other hand, there is only one stable nucleus with $N = 81$, and one with $N = 83$. Again, there are six different stable nuclei with $N = 50$, but only one each for $N = 49$ and $N = 51$. The most abundant isotope of lead is the one for which $N = 126$. Other properties have periodic variations with either maxima or minima at the magic numbers for protons or neutrons in these closed shell systems.

One way of looking at nuclear structure is to find an order in which shells are filled as nucleons are added to build heavier nuclei from lighter ones. Calculations relying on the quantum theory (page 62) have not yielded results in complete accord with known experimental facts. These facts, therefore, have been used to modify the products of theoretical calculations and help determine the order in which the shells are filled. One valuable guide appropriated from experience with electronic shell structure has been the *Pauli exclusion* principle (page 81). In this case, however, the Pauli principle is applied separately to each type of nucleon, proton, and neutron. The exclusion principle states that *no two identical particles can be in the same quantum state.*

Taking our clue once more from electronic structure, each

nucleon is assumed to move in an orbit and to revolve about an axis. Its orbital angular momentum is $lh/2\pi$ with h the Planck constant and l the orbital quantum number. It may have whole numbers from zero to $n-1$, with n the principal quantum number for the orbit. Each nucleon has an angular momentum resulting from its spin of $\frac{1}{2}h/2\pi$, with $s = \frac{1}{2}$ designated as its spin quantum number.

The total angular momentum of a nucleus may be determined experimentally (Chapter 6). Its value is designated by the letter I, once more in units of $h/2\pi$. The measurements show that for even nuclei—those in which A is equal to an even number—I is either zero or a whole number. For odd nuclei, I has odd-half values such as $1/2$, $3/2$, or $5/2$. This means that individual nucleons move with their axes parallel and spin either in the same or opposite directions.

As a simple illustration, consider the deuteron nucleus, $Z = 1$ and $N = 1$. The measured value of I is one. Since each nucleon has a spin of $1/2$, the two nucleons must be spinning in the same direction (Figure 4); that is, the vectors representing their spins point in the same direction. On the other hand, the alpha particle, or helium nucleus, $Z = 2$ and $N = 2$, has no angular momentum. From the Pauli exclusion principle, we learn that the two protons must have their spins in opposite directions and so must the two neutrons (Figure 5). The first shell, $n = 1$, has now been closed with four nucleons at magic number 2, that is, two protons and two neutrons.

Supose we take a step back and consider a nucleus with $A = 3$, namely, three nucleons. There are two nuclei of this kind: $_1H^3$ which has one proton and two neutrons, and $_2He^3$ which has two protons and one neutron. For each of these nuclei, the value

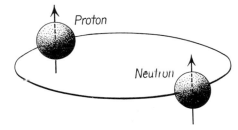

Figure 4 Proton and neutron have their spins in the same direction in a deuteron.

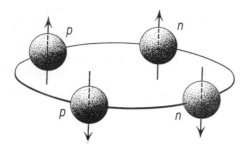

Figure 5   Alpha-particle
model. The protons have
their spins in opposite directions and so do the neutrons.

of I is known to be $1/2$. Applying the Pauli principle, the two identical particles in each nucleus have their spins oppositely oriented.

Now going forward, beyond the first completed shell, we find a nucleus with A equaling five. But no such nucleus is known to exist for any measurable length of time. The next group, $A = 6$, has two known nuclei: the stable nucleus of lithium, $_3Li^6$, and the radioactive nucleus of helium, $_2He^6$. The value for I in the case of lithium is one; thus its nuclear structure consists of a closed core of four nucleons surrounded by a proton and a neutron spinning parallel. The closed core is the alpha particle core. In contrast to lithium, the two outside nucleons of helium must have their spins opposed as, in their lowest state, they are identical particles. To date, this has not been verified experimentally.

The second shell, $n = 2$, will be filled at $Z = 8$, $N = 8$, or magic number 8. This is the structure of the most abundant isotope of oxygen. Its measured angular momentum is zero.

The assignment of nucleons can be continued on this shell model, checking against experimental data wherever possible. Much useful information is obtained from studies of nuclei of odd mass numbers. The spin quantum number of these nuclei have to be odd half-integers. We may acquire the value of I from a study of the structure of optical spectra or from measuring the magnetic moment by magnetic resonance experiments. The odd nucleon can then be assigned to the right shell.

16 FUSION AND FISSION

The energy released in various types of nuclear reactions comes, as we have seen, from the reduction in mass of the systems involved. This holds true for both natural radioactivity and artificially induced nuclear disintegrations. So far, we have been examining releases of energy of a magnitude of several million electron volts.

To get some appreciation of how enormous this quantity of energy is, suppose we compare it with the energy released in processes that are more familiar through everyday use. Burning a fuel is one of these. It may be a fuel used for heating, or for powering a gasoline engine, or it may be a blast of dynamite or TNT. In each of these actions a chemical reaction occurs bringing oxygen into combination with elements like carbon, hydrogen, and nitrogen. From the point of view of atomic physics, these reactions merely consist of a rearrangement of the outer electronic structure of carbon and oxygen, nitrogen and oxygen, and hydrogen and oxygen. And from our study of atomic structure we know that the energies of the outer electrons are rarely more than a few electron volts.

In any chemical reaction, consequently, only a few electron volts of energy are released for every molecule formed in the process. Compared with the millions of electron volts released by each nucleus involved in a nuclear reaction, the enormity of the gap between these two different sources of energy is apparent.

PRIMARY FORM OF NUCLEAR ENERGY

The form in which energy is released in nuclear reactions may be one kind or a combination of the three following kinds: (1) the kinetic energy of charged particles such as electrons, positrons, protons, alpha particles, and heavier ions; (2) the kinetic energy of neutral particles such as neutrons, neutrinos, and other particles including neutral *mesons* (to be described in Chapter 17); and (3) electromagnetic radiation in the form of gamma-ray and x-ray photons.

For special applications, as in medical therapy, the radiations are used directly and locally in the form in which they are emitted. Otherwise, it is desirable to convert this kind of energy into more controllable and more conventional products, especially into heat and electricity. The conversion into heat is relatively easy: the particles or the photons have only to be absorbed by matter. The individual processes that occur in the passage of charged particles or radiation through matter have been examined in the earlier chapters of this book. In each case, the final form of the energy is heat.

The conversion of some nuclear energy into electrical energy is possible and has been accomplished often on a small scale. The photoelectric effect is a case in point. Another simple type of direct conversion into electricity is demonstrated by the *nuclear battery* (Figure 1). It consists of two metallic plates, a small

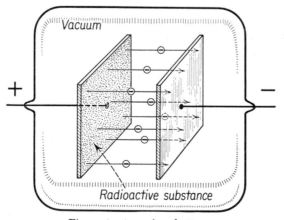

Figure 1   A nuclear battery.

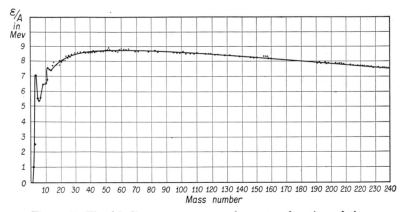

Figure 2   The binding energy per nucleon as a function of the mass number.

distance apart, placed in a vacuum chamber with a lead from each plate protruding outside. The face of one plate contains a thin layer of some radioactive substance which emits negative beta rays. These electrons strike the second plate, imparting to it a negative charge. The plate emitting these rays becomes positively charged. If a resistor or other electrical device is connected to the external leads, electrons will flow through it to the positive plate. The maximum steady current will be a saturation current (page 19) and will be proportionate to the number of electrons emitted per second. This saturation current decreases with time at a rate determined by the half-life of the radioactive isotope serving as the source. Nuclear batteries of this kind are valuable when minute amounts of power can be utilized.

Practical methods for the conversion of large amounts of nuclear energy directly into electrical energy remain to be devised. This may be done, nevertheless, by first converting the energy into heat through use of a nuclear reactor and then converting the heat into electricity through more conventional modes.

A GUIDE TO THE RELEASE OF NUCLEAR ENERGY

In searching for solutions to the problem of releasing large quantities of nuclear energy, knowledge of the binding energies of individual nuclei becomes a useful guide. Figure 2 graphically demonstrates the binding energy per nucleon $\mathcal{E}_B/A$, plotted on the vertical axis against the mass number A on the horizontal axis. The binding energy, it will be recalled, is that energy released when separate nucleons are combined to form a nucleus. The values of $\mathcal{E}_B$, the binding energy, have been obtained from measurements of the masses of the isotopes. These measurements are acquired either by use of mass spectrometers or through use of the Q-values of nuclear reactions in combination with these mass values.

One interesting aspect of the graph is that it has a maximum value for $\mathcal{E}_B/A$ which is reached approximately at $A = 60$. This value is about 8.8 Mev for each nucleon. It means that were we to bring 60 nucleons—protons and neutrons—together to form a nucleus of mass number 60, the amount of energy released would be 60×8.8, or 528 Mev. But it may not be possible to complete this in one step. We may then consider the possibility of taking two nuclei each of mass number 30 and bringing them together to form a nucleus of mass number 60. The graph lists the binding energy of a nucleon in a nucleus of mass number 30 as approximately 8.0 Mev. In forming a nucleus of mass number 30, the energy already released, as we can see, is 30×8, or 240 Mev; this totals 480 Mev for two nuclei of mass number 30. If we can create a process that will *fuse* two nuclei of mass number 30 into one nucleus of mass number 60, the energy released in this *process of fusion* would be $528 - 480$ or 48 Mev. This would still be a sizable amount of energy.

We have already reviewed several illustrations of nuclear fusion without calling them by this name. One case is the formation of a deuteron by bombarding a proton with a neutron. The amount of energy released in the process, as we saw, is 2.23 Mev for each deuteron created. Another fusion process is the capture of a proton by a nucleus of mass number less than 60 without the subsequent emission of a particle. This is usually called a p-γ reaction. The capture of a proton by aluminum, $A = 27$, to form silicon, $A = 28$, exemplifies this process. Here the mass difference is equivalent to 2.28 Mev and is radiated in the form of a gamma-ray photon.

As a practical matter, the problem is not one of producing single reactions in which energy is released. It is a problem of finding the conditions under which a chain of reactions, or a cycle of reactions, can be maintained to assure the continuation of the release of energy at a predetermined rate. A guide to this may be found in the sun and the stars.

FUSION OF HYDROGEN INTO HELIUM

Spectroscopic analysis of the light from the sun and the stars shows that they contain large quantities of hydrogen. This led Hans Bethe to propose an hypothesis in 1939 that the fusion of hydrogen into helium is one of the most important sources of stellar energy. Ordinarily it would take four atoms of hydrogen to form a helium atom. The mass liberated as energy would be $4 \times 1.00815 - 4.00388$, or 0.02872 atomic mass units, which is equivalent to 26.7 million electron volts for every atom of helium thus formed.

Bethe suggested two possible series of reactions whereby the fusion of hydrogen into helium could occur. One is known as the *proton-proton chain* and begins with the collision of two protons that form a deuteron. This reaction may be written as

$$_1H^1 + {}_1H^1 \rightarrow {}_1H^2 + \beta^+.$$

This is followed by another reaction between another proton and the deuteron to yield helium, $A = 3$:

$$_1H^1 + {}_1H^2 \rightarrow {}_2He^3.$$

The chain then continues with one of the following two probable reactions:

$$_1H^1 + {}_2He^3 \rightarrow {}_2He^4 + \beta^+$$

or $\qquad {}_2He^3 + {}_2He^3 \rightarrow {}_2Hc^4 + {}_1H^1 + {}_1H^1.$

Another series of fusion reactions in which protons form helium nuclei depends on the availability of carbon and nitrogen as nuclear catalysts to initiate and maintain the cycle of reactions. This series, the carbon-nitrogen cycle, may be written as

$$_6C^{12} + {}_1H^1 \rightarrow {}_7N^{13} + \text{gamma rays}$$

followed by $\qquad {}_7N^{13} \rightarrow {}_6C^{13} + \beta^+$

then $\qquad {}_6C^{13} + {}_1H^1 \rightarrow {}_7N^{14} + \text{gamma rays}$

and $\qquad {}_7N^{14} + {}_1H^1 \rightarrow {}_8O^{15} + \text{gamma rays}$

followed by $\qquad {}_8O^{15} \rightarrow {}_7N^{15} + \beta^+$

and $\qquad {}_7N^{15} + {}_1H^1 \rightarrow {}_6C^{12} + {}_2He^4.$

The end product of this series is carbon, $A = 12$, and helium. The cycle may now begin anew. It may also start with nitrogen, $A = 14$.

It has been estimated that the sun contains about 2×10^{23} protons for every gram of its mass. The rate at which the sun radiates energy at present is also known. Were the sun to continue to radiate at its present rate, it would take about thirty billion years to exhaust its supply of protons.

STELLAR EVOLUTION

Speculation about the evolution of the stars is a fascinating pastime. It is agreed in general that the first stage is the contraction of a large mass of tenuous matter from a large cloud of gas to a more compact star; this takes place under the action of the gravitational attraction of its particles. As a result, a higher temperature is produced at the center of the star. This temperature generates a flow of heat toward the surface and sparks radiation of energy from the star.

At some stage in the contraction process the temperature at the center of the star must become high enough to induce collisions between nuclei. These collisions require sufficient kinetic energy to initiate nuclear reactions with a consequent liberation of energy. Also they must occur with enough frequency to account for the rate at which energy is known to be radiated by different classes of stars. With our present knowledge about the likelihood of various types of nuclear reactions taking place, we are able to estimate the rate at which a star radiates energy under a host of temperature and density conditions. For the sun, for example, it has been estimated that the rate of generation of energy in the proton-proton chain is about the same as in the carbon-nitrogen cycle. For much more luminous stars, the carbon-nitrogen cycle predominates.

When all the hydrogen is exhausted in the foregoing *thermonuclear* reactions, the star will consist mainly of helium. The temperature in the star is not high enough to touch off nuclear reactions among the helium nuclei. At this point gravitational attraction recurs until a temperature of 100,000,000 degrees is reached with the density of the star about 10,000 times greater than water. Under these conditions three helium nuclei will fuse to form carbon, $A = 12$, with the release of about 7.3 Mev for each carbon nucleus formed.

When all the helium is consumed, further gravitational contraction will occur, raising the temperature of the star still higher so that conditions obtain for the formation of nuclei of medium atomic masses. A glance at Figure 2 shows that the maximum temperature will be reached when the atoms formed have masses of the magnitude of $A = 60$. H. Bondi and E. E. Salpeter in tracing this life history of a star suggested in 1952 that in forming atoms of heavier mass than 60, energy must be absorbed in the reactions, causing a sudden collapse of the star. This collapse may be identified as the sudden appearance of a *super nova* with a tremendous liberation of energy in a comparatively short time interval, followed by equally sudden cooling and disappearance from view.

The processes in the stars suggest methods for producing similar behaviors on earth. This has been accomplished successfully in the so-called hydrogen bomb. Studies are now under way to harness this tremendous supply of energy produced by fusion processes for the benefit of mankind, mainly in the form of power for peaceful purposes.

DISCOVERY OF NUCLEAR FISSION

In the present state of knowledge it is easy to see that another method for the release of nuclear energy (Figure 2) would be the splitting of a heavy nucleus, such as $A = 240$, into two nuclei with mass numbers in the range from 60 to 180. Historically the discovery of this process was accidental.

Beginning in 1934, Enrico Fermi and his co-workers bombarded uranium with neutrons in an attempt to produce elements of atomic number greater than 92. They found that as a result of such bombardments some of the uranium was converted into elements which emitted beta particles with various half-lives. It will be recalled that natural uranium, the first radioactive element ever discovered, disintegrates with the emission of alpha particles; these beta-ray activities indicated that some new process was taking place. This new process was interpreted as the formation of one or more *transuranic elements,* that is, elements of atomic number greater than 92. Chemical tests performed to verify this hypothesis made it seem fairly certain that an element of atomic number 93 was produced. However, chemical analysis for elements in this part of the periodic table is very difficult and these results were not completely convincing.

Other workers, particularly Irene Curie and her co-workers, and Hahn, Strassmann, and Meitner, entered this field in search of transuranic elements. The heavy elements—uranium, thorium, and protactinium—were bombarded with neutrons, and new elements were produced which disintegrated with the emission of beta rays. These elements were generally assigned atomic numbers greater than 92. In an effort to identify them more accurately, physical and chemical experiments were made on the small amounts of new elements produced.

In 1939, Hahn and Strassmann found, after a series of chemical experiments, that one of the radioactive elements produced by the bombardment of uranium by neutrons was an isotope of barium of atomic number 56. Another of the radioactive elements formed this way was identified as lanthanum, atomic number 57. This was a very startling discovery. Hahn and Strassmann suggested that the beta-ray activities previously observed and ascribed to transuranic elements were probably emitted by radioactive isotopes of elements of lower atomic number, that is, elements in the middle of the periodic table.

The process begun by bombarding uranium with neutrons is one in which the new uranium nucleus formed by the capture of a neutron is unstable, and splits into two nuclei of medium atomic masses (Figure 3). If one nucleus which is produced in this process is barium, atomic number 56, the other must be the nucleus of the element krypton, atomic number 36, since the total charge of the uranium nucleus is 92. This type of distintegration process in which a heavy nucleus splits up into two nuclei of nearly comparable masses is called *nuclear fission*.

As soon as the discovery of nuclear fission was announced early in 1939, physicists in laboratories throughout the world where neutron sources were available immediately repeated and confirmed these experiments. Cloud-chamber pictures were obtained, showing the tracks of the two particles (produced by the fission of uranium) traveling in opposite directions (Figure 4).

The masses of the fission products are found to be those of unstable isotopes; that is, they have many more neutrons than

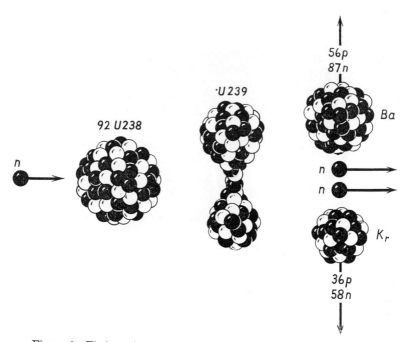

Figure 3 Fission of uranium. A fast neutron is captured by a nucleus of uranium 238 forming uranium 239. The latter becomes unstable and splits into two comparatively massive particles, in the above case krypton and barium, with the simultaneous emission of two fast neutrons.

the stable isotopes of the corresponding elements. One of the first questions investigated was the manner in which these unstable fission products disintegrated, particularly whether any of the excess neutrons were emitted in this process. Early experiments showed that between two and three neutrons were emitted per nuclear fission (Figure 3).

A variety of other pairs of nuclei may be produced in the fission process. All of them are radioactive, most of them decaying to a stable form by the emission of beta rays. Gamma rays are also emitted by many of these isotopes. These are known as the fission products (Figure 5).

In addition to uranium, thorium, $Z = 90$, and protactinium, $Z = 91$, have been found to be fissionable by the capture of neutrons; also a new element, plutonium, $Z = 94$. Fission may also occur spontaneously, by excitation of a nucleus with high-energy

Figure 4   Cloud-chamber photograph showing the fission of uranium.
The foil in the center of the cloud chamber is coated with uranium and
bombarded by neutrons. The tracks of the two heavy fission particles can
be seen coming from the foil where a uranium atom has undergone fission
as the result of the capture of a neutron. (*From a photograph by J. K.
Boggild, K. K. Brostom, and T. Lauritsen.*)

gamma rays and by bombardment of heavy nuclei with protons,
deuterons, or alpha particles. In the following sections, we shall
discuss only neutron-induced nuclear fission.

A NUCLEAR CHAIN REACTION

The concept of a nuclear chain reaction is very simple: if
a single nuclear-fission process involving the capture of one
neutron results in the release of energy and simultaneously the
release of more than one neutron, it should be possible so to
arrange the mass of fissionable material to ensure the capture
of the newly released neutrons. Put another way, the mass of
fissionable material should be so arranged that at any one place
the number of new neutrons produced should be equal to the
number of free neutrons originally present there. The ratio of
these two numbers of neutrons is called the *multiplication factor*
K. If $K = 1$, the chain reaction will be self-sustaining; if K is
less than 1, the process will ultimately come to a halt; if K is
greater than 1, the neutron density will increase and may lead to
an explosive reaction. A mass of fissionable material so arranged

that the multiplication factor is equal to or greater than 1 constitutes a nuclear reactor.

In order to be able to design a nuclear reactor, it is essential to know the conditions under which neutrons are captured by nuclei and under which the capture results in the fission of the product nuclei. We shall restrict this discussion to the fission of uranium.

Ordinary uranium consists of three isotopes: one of mass number 238, another of mass number 235, and a third of mass number 234. The most abundant of these is U238—about 99.3 per cent abundance. The amount of U234 in ordinary uranium

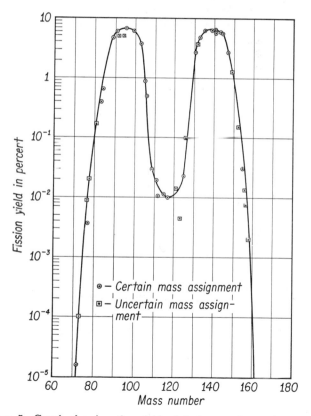

Figure 5 Graph showing the yield of fission products of uranium 235 as a function of their mass number. (*After "Plutonium Project Report on Nuclei Formed in Fission"*, Rev. Modern Phys., *18, 539, 1946.*)

is negligible. U235 constitutes about 0.7 per cent of ordinary uranium. Experiments show that U238 is fissionable only if it captures fast neutrons, that is, neutrons having energies of 1 Mev or greater. On the other hand, U235 is fissionable with neutrons of any speed and particularly with slow neutrons, that is, neutrons having energies corresponding to the energies at ordinary temperatures which are much less than 1 Mev.

The neutrons released in nuclear fission have a wide range of energies. In the case of the fission of U235, these energies extend up to about 17 Mev, with a maximum number having energies of about 0.75 Mev. If such neutrons are captured by other uranium nuclei, they produce nuclear fission. However, not every collision between a fast neutron and a uranium nucleus results in capture of the neutron; the collision may simply produce a decrease in the energy of the neutron. Thereafter the probability of its capture will be very small; additional collisions will produce further reductions in the energy of the neutrons. At some particular values of energy, the neutron will be readily captured by U238, but this does not result in nuclear fission. Instead, a newly formed isotope of uranium, U239, emits a gamma-ray photon and then becomes radioactive, emitting a beta ray with a half-life of 23 min. The nuclear reaction equations are

$$_{92}U^{238} + {}_0n^1 \rightarrow {}_{92}U^{239} \rightarrow {}_{92}U^{239} + \text{gamma ray},$$

then $$_{92}U^{239} \rightarrow {}_{93}Np^{239} + \beta^-.$$

The new element formed, called neptunium, Np, is itself radioactive, emitting a beta particle with a half-life of 2.3 days. The product nucleus formed in this reaction is plutonium, Pu, atomic number 94. The reaction in which this is formed is

$$_{93}Np^{239} \rightarrow {}_{94}Pu^{239} + \beta^-.$$

It is followed by

$$_{94}Pu^{239} \rightarrow {}_{92}U^{235} + {}_2He^4.$$

The isotope of plutonium is radioactive, emitting an alpha particle, but it has a very long half-life—24,000 years. In this sense, it is a comparatively stable element. When plutonium disintegrates with the emission of an alpha particle, the resulting nucleus is U235. The plutonium isotope formed in the process is fissionable by the capture of neutrons of any energy and is thus similar to U235 as far as the fission process is concerned. Since it is chemically different from uranium, it can be separated more readily from the uranium metal than the uranium isotope of mass number 235.

The first nuclear reactor, or uranium pile as it is sometimes called, was operated successfully in Chicago on December 2, 1942; it was built under the direction of Fermi and operated by groups headed by W. H. Zinn and H. L. Anderson. A schematic diagram of the construction of a uranium pile is shown in Figure 6. Rods of uranium metal are embedded in blocks of graphite; rods of boron metal are inserted at various places in the pile to control the flux of neutrons; boron nuclei capture neutrons readily. No special source of neutrons is needed to start this pile; there are always neutrons present from cosmic rays, or from spontaneous fission, to start the nuclear reactor. The mode of its operation can be understood by referring to Figure 7.

Suppose that a neutron is captured by a uranium nucleus, so that fission results and that two new neutrons are released with energies of about 1 Mev each. These neutrons then make

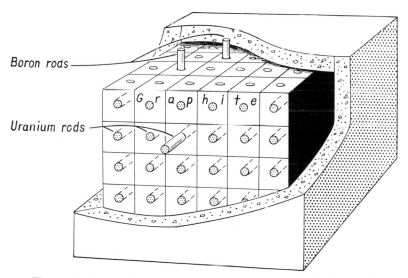

Figure 6 Schematic diagram of a uranium pile. Cylindrical rods of uranium are embedded in a large mass of graphite which acts as a moderator to slow down neutrons. Boron rods, which are inserted into the pile, control its rate of activity.

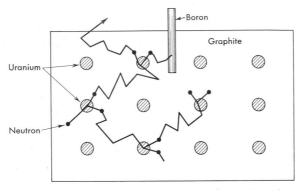

Figure 7 Schematic diagram of the action of a neutron in a uranium pile based on the assumption that each fission process yields two neutrons. The shaded circles represent rods of uranium; the small circular dots represent neutrons. Sudden changes in direction of the neutron path are due to collisions with nuclei of the moderator graphite.

several collisions with nuclei of the moderator—a light element in which the probability of capture of a neutron is unlikely, but in which collisions between neutrons and nuclei will decrease the neutron's energy; in this case graphite—until their energies are reduced to thermal energies. Whenever one of these slow neutrons is captured by U235, fission will again occur with the release of, say, two neutrons. Some neutrons may be lost through the surface of the reactor; one way to reduce this loss is to make the reactor very large. The increase in the surface area is proportionate to the square of its linear dimension, while the volume is in proportion to the cube of the linear dimension.

Other neutrons may be lost through capture by impurities or through nonfissionable capture by U238. But if $K = 1$, the reaction will be self-sustaining. To prevent the multiplication factor from becoming excessive, boron rods are inserted to various depths in the uranium pile to absorb the excess neutrons. One other control factor may be mentioned: that is, not all of the neutrons are emitted promptly in nuclear fission; a small percentage of them are delayed, some by 0.01 sec, others by as much as 1 min.

A whole new field of nuclear science and engineering has been opened as the result of the discovery of nuclear fission and following the successful construction of the first nuclear reactor.

Nuclear reactors designed for many different purposes are now in operation throughout the world. Some are used as sources of energy for power plants; others are used for experimental purposes. A nuclear reactor is one of the best sources of neutrons for use in physical, chemical, and biological experiments. It is also a source of radioactive isotopes for medical and industrial uses. A nuclear reactor may also be designed as a military weapon known as an atomic bomb or A-bomb. The latter is a type of nuclear reactor in which the multiplication factor K is greater than 1. It may consist of uranium containing a large percentage of U235 or of plutonium 239. If the mass of fissionable material is less than a certain critical amount, K will be less than 1, and there will be no chain reaction. If the mass is built up rapidly so that the total exceeds the critical mass, a very fast chain reaction will be produced. One of the problems in exploding an atomic bomb is to hold the material together for a sufficient time, probably several millionths of a second, so that a large quantity of the material will take part in the fission process. It has been estimated that the energy released in an atomic bomb is sufficient to raise the temperature of this material to several million degrees and to produce pressures upon explosion of perhaps a few million atmospheres. In this process, great quantities of radioactive materials and gamma rays are also produced.

17 NEW ADVENTURES IN PHYSICS

For about thirty years prior to 1932, the atom was assumed to consist of only two fundamental, stable particles—electrons and protons. In the Bohr-Rutherford picture of nuclear structure, the atom contained A electrons and A protons, with A designating the mass number. The A protons were all in the nucleus along with $A - Z$ electrons; the Z electrons remained outside the nucleus of the neutralized atom whose atomic number was Z. This picture changed radically in 1932 with the discovery of the neutron. The number of electrons outside the atom remained the same, but there were no longer any electrons inside the nucleus. Instead, N neutrons took their place along with Z protons; thus N became $A - Z$, or $A = Z - N$.

After 1932, the number of subatomic, or *elementary particles* as they may be called, began to increase at a rapid rate. There are now about 20 of them (Figure 1). Many of these particles were first discovered through experiments with cosmic rays. Some of them also have been produced by the nuclear reactions induced by high-energy particles and radiation now obtainable in several laboratories around the world.

These particles all have electric charges of zero or one, in terms of the electronic charge e. The charges of all other known particles are whole numbers of e; that is, they are quantized in units of e. Figure 1 groups the elementary particles in three vertical columns according to their charge: $+e$, 0, or $-e$. The masses of the particles are listed on the vertical scale in units of electronic mass m_e. The particles of intermediate mass, be-

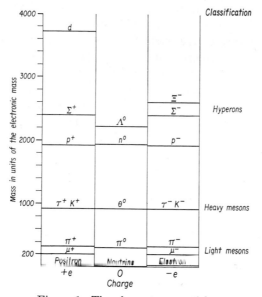

Figure 1   The elementary particles.

tween the masses of the neutron and the electron, are generally called *mesons*. Those whose masses fall between the neutron's and that of the first complex particle, deuteron (*d*), are known as *hyperons*.

Some of these particles are stable; for example, the electron, the positron, the proton, the antiproton, and the neutrino. The others are all unstable, with very short lifetimes for many of them. In this chapter, we shall examine the modes of decay, methods of production, and the determination of some of the properties of these particles. We shall also endeavor to show how some of them fit into the scheme of nuclear events.

COSMIC RAYS

In the early part of the twentieth century, electroscopes were used extensively in experiments on x-rays and radioactivity. Researchers quickly noted that even though there was no known radiation present in the vicinity of an electroscope nor any known discharge taking place in a circuit nearby, a charged electroscope would gradually lose its charge. They surmised that the discharge of a carefully shielded, well-insulated electroscope could be produced only by some type of radiation which came either from below the surface of the earth or from outside the atmosphere.

About 1910, experiments were begun to test the foregoing hypothesis. Investigators measured the rate of discharge at different altitudes above the earth's crust. W. Kolhorster and V. F. Hess found, in 1912, that a charged electroscope's rate of discharge decreased at first as the altitude increased, but then, beginning at 700 meters, started to climb. These observations led to the opinion that whatever radiations were causing the discharge of the electroscope must have come from outside the earth; hence the name *cosmic rays*. Since these rays came through the atmosphere it was felt that they must possess strong penetrating power. Experiments in which cosmic rays had to penetrate additional thicknesses of absorbing materials before reaching the detector added verification.

Studies of cosmic rays were largely halted during World War I, but resumed immediately afterward. At that time it was believed they were very penetrating (high frequency) gamma rays. In 1927, however, J. Clay observed that the intensity of cosmic rays at sea level was not constant, but that it varied with changes in latitude. This was taken to mean that cosmic rays must contain some charged particles whose motions and paths were affected by the earth's magnetic field. A group of observers headed by A. H. Compton and stationed throughout the world at various laboratories confirmed this latitude phenomenon by a series of measurements made between 1930 and 1933.

The present view of the nature of the cosmic rays is that they are highly energetic nuclei originating outside the atmosphere. These *primary* cosmic rays, as they are called, are mostly protons but also contain some heavier nuclei, some with charges greater than $40e$ (Figure 2). To study these particular rays, it is necessary to send experimental equipment aloft by balloon to altitudes above 60,000 feet. The equipment may consist of automatically operated cloud chambers, or stacks of photographic plates with nuclear emulsions, or stacks of nuclear emulsions without the glass plate backing. When the equipment is recovered, the events it has recorded can then be studied.

The primary cosmic ray particles must possess large amounts

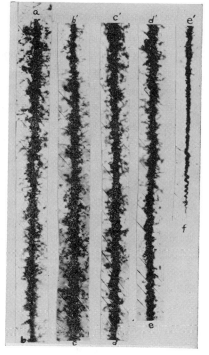

Figure 2   Photomicrograph of a heavy nucleus in the primary cosmic rays. The nuclear charge is about 42e. It was observed in a stack of photographic emulsions without glass plate backing. The primary particle entered the stack at a and slowed down in traveling 1.80 mm through the emulsion in a continuous path abb'cc'dd'ee'f. The corkscrew effect observed at the end of the path is due to the buckling of the column of developed silver as the emulsion shrinks during processing. (*Photomicrograph courtesy of Maurice M. Shapiro and Nathan Seeman, Naval Research Laboratory.*)

of energy to pass through the broad magnetic field of the earth and enter the atmosphere. For example, protons must have energies of more than 2.5 billion electron volts to reach the earth's atmosphere vertically at a magnetic latitude of 45 degrees North. Heavier nuclei, because of their heavier charge, have to possess even greater energies—perhaps in excess of 100,000 Mev—in order to penetrate the earth's magnetic field. Other estimates of the energies of cosmic-ray particles run as high as 10^9 Mev.

Most cosmic-ray particles observed in the atmosphere, however, are of *secondary* origin. They are the products of the interaction between the primary cosmic-ray particles and nuclei in the atmosphere. The discoveries of many of the new particles of physics have resulted from investigations of such events. We have already considered one of these, the discovery of the positron in 1932 by Carl D. Anderson. We shall discuss several others later in the chapter.

MATERIALIZATION OF ENERGY

The discovery of the positron in a cosmic-ray experiment actually had been predicted in 1928, four years before Anderson's achievement, by P. A. M. Dirac in his quantum theory of the electron. Solutions of Dirac's equations show that electrons can exist in either of two sets of energy states, one set having positive energies greater than $+ m_e c^2$, the other having negative energies below $- m_e c^2$, with m_e signifying electronic rest-mass. At that time, with only electrons and protons known to scientists, the foregoing results were not understood clearly. But with the discovery of the positron in 1932, it became apparent that the value of $+ m_e c^2$ corresponded to the energies of the electron and that $- m_e c^2$ must correspond to the energy of an oppositely charged particle, the *positron*. The positron is sometimes alluded to as the *antiparticle* of the electron.

Shortly after discovery of the positron, cloud-chamber photographs of certain cosmic-ray events showed the presence of electrons and positrons. This indicated that a particle-antiparticle pair had a common origin. The theory developed to explain this observation was that a photon with an energy more than $2m_e c^2$ could be converted into a pair of particles through interaction with a strong electric field such as the kind that exists in the vicinity of a nucleus or an electron.

Figure 3   Cloud-chamber photograph of the paths of an electron-positron pair, formed by the disintegration of a 5.7 gamma-ray photon in its passage through a thin sheet of lead. The magnetic field is directed into the paper. (*Photograph by H. R. Crane.*)

Since the rest-mass energy of an electron is equivalent to 0.51 Mev, whether positive or negative, a photon needs minimum energy of 1.02 Mev to create a pair. Figure 3 is a cloud-chamber photograph that shows the tracks of an electron-positron pair formed by the conversion of a gamma-ray photon of 5.7 Mev as it passes near a nucleus in the lead sheet in the chamber. The tracks curve in opposite directions because of the action of the magnetic field whose direction runs into the page. The measured values of the kinetic energies of the electron-positron pair is 4.7 Mev. Together with the rest-mass energy, 1.02 Mev, this equals the photon's energy.

This process of pair-production from radiation is often called the *materialization of energy.* To satisfy the principle of conservation of charge, the particles formed must have equal and opposite charges. Recently this pair-formation process was also seen in the production of positive and negative mu-mesons, μ^+ and μ^-, from gamma-ray photons.

The production of pairs of charged particles is another fundamental process whereby gamma rays release energy in their passage through matter. The others are the photoelectric and the Compton effects. The pair-production process we have been discussing is used often to measure gamma-ray energies in excess of 1.02 Mev.

THE ANNIHILATION OF MATTER

The reverse of pair formation is the combination of an electron and a positron into a gamma-ray photon. This process is the *annihilation of matter.* When a positron passes through a substance it loses energy by collisions and when its velocity is just about zero it will combine with an electron. Because it is repelled by the positive charge of the nucleus, it combines more often with an outer electron, or a free electron. In such cases, the combination of the pair results in production of two gamma-ray photons, each with an energy $m_e c^2$ of 0.511 Mev. From use of the equation for the energy of the photon

$$h\nu = c/\lambda$$

we obtain for the wavelength of this radiation

$$\lambda = h/m_e c$$

which is the same as the Compton wavelength (page 117). The wavelength of this annihilation radiation has been measured by Jesse W. DuMond and co-workers with a crystal spectrometer of high precision and found to be in agreement with other precise measurements of the Compton wavelength.

THE EXISTENCE OF MESONS

The nature of the force between nucleons is still one of the most important and yet baffling mysteries of nuclear physics. In 1935, a Japanese physicist, H. Yukawa, made a significant step toward understanding it. Yukawa postulated the existence of a nuclear field of force called a *mesonic field* that acts between nucleons. The field has particles associated with it in much the same way as photons are associated with the electromagnetic field which exists between charged particles. These particles associated with the mesonic field are called *mesons*. According to Yukawa's theory, a meson should have an intermediate mass between a proton's and an electron's. A meson can be negative, positive, or neutral.

A particle called a *mu-meson* (μ-*meson*) or *muon*, with a mass of 207 m_e, was discovered in 1937 during cloud-chamber studies of cosmic rays. This particle has an average lifetime of 2.15×10^{-6} sec before its spontaneous decay into an electron. This lifetime is much greater than Yukawa's theory predicted. It was generally agreed that this was not the particle needed to support the theory of meson forces.

World War II interrupted work on this problem. After the war, physicists studying cosmic rays renewed the hunt for the Yukawa meson. One method of search was to expose nuclear photographic emulsions at high altitudes. The first evidence of the existence of such heavy mesons, called *pi-mesons* (π-*mesons*), was found in 1947. Figure 4 depicts one of the unusual events photographed high above the earth's surface. It shows a negative pi-meson, captured in the emulsion, giving rise to a *star* as three particles are liberated. Another process discovered with such plates was the disintegration of a pi-meson, also called a *pion*, into a mu-meson which, in turn, disintegrated into an electron. The mass of the charged pi-meson is 273m_e.

By this time, the first of the frequency-modulated cyclotrons

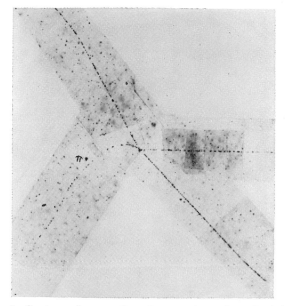

Figure 4   Capture of a negative pi meson (curved track on lower left) by a nucleus producing a star in a photograph emulsion. (*Photograph by D. H. Perkins*, Nature, *159, 126, 1947*.)

was in operation at the University of California. It was capable of producing alpha particles of 380 Mev energy. Alpha particles of this energy were used to bombard such targets as carbon or beryllium in an effort to obtain mesons (Figure 5). Negative pi-mesons were thus produced; they traveled in a semicircular path

Figure 5   Schematic diagram of the apparatus in the first experiment of the production of pi mesons using 380 Mev alpha particles of the 184-inch California University synchrocyclotron to bombard a target.

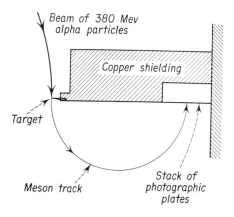

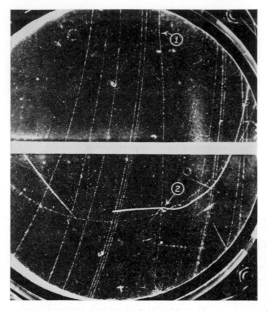

Figure 6 Photograph of tracks of negative pi mesons and associated events in a cloud-chamber placed in a magnetic field. At (1) negative pi meson decays in flight into a mu meson. At (2) a meson, which lost some energy in a brass bolt, came to rest in the gas and was captured by a nucleus, resulting in a nuclear explosion forming a *star*. (*Photograph courtesy of L. Lederman, Nevis Cyclotron Laboratory, Columbia University.*)

in the magnetic field of the cyclotron and were recorded on photographic plates.

Other cyclotrons producing high-energy particles, usually protons, came into operation shortly thereafter and these also were used to obtain pi-mesons. Figure 6 shows a cloud-chamber photograph of negative pi-mesons in a magnetic field illustrating two typical events: (1) the decay in flight of a pi-meson into a mu-meson; and (2) a negative pi-meson slowed down (indicated by thickness of track) and then captured by a nucleus resulting in a nuclear explosion that forms a star. Figure 7 shows a cloud-chamber photograph of a positive pi-meson in a magnetic field. Of marked interest is the slowing down of a positive pi-meson (path *A*) and its disintegration at point 1 into a positive mu-meson (path *D*); the mu-meson passes into a carbon block where it decays into a positron which emerges from the block (path E).

The pi-mesons may be produced by bombarding the nucleons in a target with high-energy projectiles such as protons or with gamma-ray photons. Not only have positive and negative pi-mesons been produced, but neutral pi-mesons as well. The mass of the neutral pi-meson is smaller than the charged type by about $10m_e$. In addition, the neutral pi-meson decays into two gamma-ray photons in less than 10^{-14} sec, whereas the average lifetime of a charged pi-meson is 1.75×10^{-8} sec.

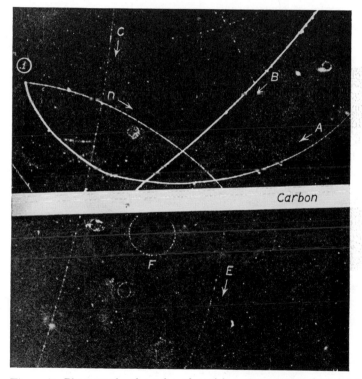

Figure 7 Photograph of tracks of positive pi mesons and associated events in a cloud-chamber placed in a magnetic field. A slow pi meson (track A) comes to rest in the gas at (1) and decays into a positive mu meson moving along track D. It enters carbon plate and decays into a positron (track E). C is track of positive pi meson and B is path of a proton. (*Photograph courtesy of L. Lederman, Nevis Cyclotron Laboratory, Columbia University.*)

ELEMENTARY PROCESSES

As we have noted, neutral particles do not leave visible tracks in the devices used for detection in nuclear physics. Their presence has to be inferred by application of fundamental physical laws to the processes under consideration. These laws are worth restating. They are: (1) the law of conservation of energy; (2) the law of conservation of electric charge; (3) the law of conservation of linear momentum; and (4) the law of the conservation of angular momentum.

In almost every process involving elementary particles, the velocities are of the magnitude of the speed of light. Therefore the fundamental laws of physics must be applied in their relativistic sense. For example, mass must be considered as a form of energy, and all these processes have to obey the quantum rules.

In terms of these fundamental laws, let us reconsider the process of beta decay. We have shown that a negative beta particle or electron is emitted in the decay of a neutron into a proton. To conserve energy in this process, a neutral particle, the neutrino (ν), was introduced. But there is a much more important reason for its introduction: Each elementary particle, the electron, the proton, and the neutron, has angular momentum normally related to its spin. The value of the angular momentum for each is $\frac{1}{2}h/2\pi$, with h the Planck constant and $h/2\pi$ the unit of angular momentum. We refer to this angular momentum by saying it has a spin of $1/2$.

The principle of conservation of angular momentum applied to a process states that the total spin of the initial particles must equal the total spin, or angular momentum, of the final particles. Thus the process of beta decay may be expressed as

$$n \rightarrow p + e^- + \nu$$

with spin $1/2 \rightarrow 1/2 + 1/2 - 1/2.$

The emission of a positron by a proton can be treated the same way:

$$p \rightarrow n + e^+ + \nu$$

with spin $1/2 \rightarrow 1/2 - 1/2 + 1/2.$

Sometimes these two neutrinos, the one emitted in electron

decay and the other in positron decay, are considered as two components of *one* neutrino; the one accompanying the electron emission is sometimes called the *antineutrino*.

The neutrino is a particle without charge and practically no rest-mass. But it has a spin of 1/2 and does possess energy. Its existence has been established beyond doubt in experiments by F. Reines and C. L. Cowan, Jr., between 1953 and 1956. They utilized the large supply of neutrinos continuously emitted in beta decay of the fission fragments formed in a large nuclear reactor. The neutrinos were allowed to enter a large liquid scintillation counter. Some of them interacted with the hydrogen in the liquid to form the following reaction:

$$\nu + p \rightarrow n + e^{+}.$$

Both the neutron and the positron were detected.

Applying the conservation laws to the decay of a mu-meson into an electron, we find that two neutrinos of opposite spin must be emitted simultaneously:

$$\mu^{\pm} \rightarrow e^{\pm} + \nu + \nu.$$

The pi-meson, on the other hand, has a spin of zero. Therefore its decay into a mu-meson requires emission of only one neutrino:

$$\pi^{\pm} \rightarrow \mu^{\pm} + \nu.$$

The negative mesons, both mu and pi, during passage through matter will be slowed down and may be captured in orbits surrounding nuclei. In this case, they will form types of Bohr atoms called *mesic atoms*. We have seen that the radius of a Bohr orbit (chapter 4) varies inversely with the mass of the negatively charged particle. The radius of the orbit of a mesic atom consequently will be 1/200 or 1/300 of an electronic atom. The energies of the mesic atom will be correspondingly higher so that transitions from one mesic orbit to another will result in the emission of x-ray photons. The liberation of x-rays has been observed from both mu-mesic and pi-mesic atoms.

The heavy mesons, also called K-particles, have been noted in cosmic rays and also produced in proton bombardment of targets in the Cosmotron and Bevatron. Their mass is $966.5m_e$ for each particle and they have no spin. These mesons have different modes of disintegration. Sometimes they decay into three pi-mesons, each of zero spin, and sometimes into a mu-meson of spin 1/2 and probably a neutrino, spin 1/2. Figure 8 shows the latter mode; it contains the tracks of protons and K-mesons, one depicting K-μ decay, formed in a *bubble chamber*.

The bubble chamber, developed in 1953 by Donald A. Glaser, is one of the newest devices for study of reactions among high-energy particles. It consists of a superheated liquid kept under pressure. When a charged particle passes through the liquid, it forms ions along its path. These ions serve as centers for the formation of vapor bubbles. A slight reduction in pressure of the liquid causes the bubbles to grow large enough to be photographed.

NUCLEONS AND ANTINUCLEONS

Dirac's theory of the electron which led to the conclusion that there should be a pair of electrons may be extended to show that there should be a pair of protons, positive and negative. The negative proton is called the *antiproton*. It should have the same mass and spin as the proton, but a charge of opposite sign. If an antiproton is to be produced by a collision of two protons, the impinging proton should have an energy of 5,600 Mev (5.6 billion electron volts or 5.6 Bev). This was one of the aims in designing a 6 Bev proton accelerator at the University of California.

Figure 8   Photograph showing tracks of charged particles in a bubble chamber. The short, heavy tracks are produced by protons which stop in the chamber. The disintegration of a positive K-particle into a positive mu meson is also shown. (*Phtograph courtesy of Donald A. Glaser.*)

Evidence for the existence of antiprotons was obtained from cosmic-ray experiments, but the first production of *antinucleons* came in 1955 in an experiment performed by O. Chamberlain, E. Segrè, C. Wiegand, and T. Ypsilantis which used the 6.2 Bev proton beam of the Bevatron. The copper target that was struck by these protons emitted negatively charged particles that were deflected out of the accelerator by its magnetic field. Most of the beam consisted of pi-mesons, mu-mesons, and electrons. About one in 50,000 particles turned out to be an antiproton. This was separated from the remainder of the beam by a mass spectrometer containing a velocity selector. The velocity of the antiproton was 0.78c in comparison with the mesons' velocities of about 0.99c.

The antiproton, moving in a vacuum, is a stable particle. In passing through matter, however, it combines with a proton and the two are annihilated. Their combined energies, about 2,600 Mev, appear mostly in the form of pi-mesons which in a photographic emulsion look like a star (Figure 9). As we have seen before, these particles decay and their energies ultimately are transformed into gamma-ray photons.

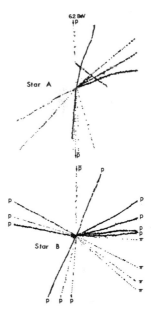

Figure 9   A 6.2 Bev proton produces a star at A in the nuclear emulsion. An antiproton p^- from this star travels 1.4 mm in the emulsion and is annihilated producing 14 visible particles, protons (p) and mesons (π). The total energy of these particles is 1460 Mev. (*Photograph courtesy of R. D. Hill, S. D. Johansson, and F. T. Gardner, Phys. Rev., 103, 250, 1956.*)

The existence of an *antineutron* also has been inferred from experiments. In these, the track of an antiproton in a bubble chamber ends suddenly, and further on, a star appears. The interpretation of this phenomenon is that the antiproton transfers its charge to a proton to form a neutron. The remaining antineutron itself leaves no track, but annihilates with a neutron to produce a star.

GREEK ALPHABET

Lower-case Letter	Capital Letter	Name of Letter
α	A	alpha
β	B	beta
γ	Γ	gamma
δ	Δ	delta
ϵ	E	epsilon
ζ	Z	zeta
η	H	eta
θ	Θ	theta
ι	I	iota
κ	K	kappa
λ	Λ	lambda
μ	M	mu
ν	N	nu
ξ	Ξ	xi
o	O	omicron
π	Π	pi
ρ	P	rho
σ, ς	Σ	sigma
τ	T	tau
υ	Υ	upsilon
ϕ	Φ	phi
χ	X	chi
ψ	Ψ	psi
ω	Ω	omega

INDEX

INDEX